Oxaprozin loaded solid lipid nanop...

Vinod K. Dhote
Kanika Dhote

Oxaprozin loaded solid lipid nanoparticles for management of pain

Novel Development of Oxaprozin loaded Solid Lipid Nanoparticles for effective management of pain

LAP LAMBERT Academic Publishing

Imprint
Any brand names and product names mentioned in this book are subject to trademark, brand or patent protection and are trademarks or registered trademarks of their respective holders. The use of brand names, product names, common names, trade names, product descriptions etc. even without a particular marking in this work is in no way to be construed to mean that such names may be regarded as unrestricted in respect of trademark and brand protection legislation and could thus be used by anyone.

Cover image: www.ingimage.com

Publisher:
LAP LAMBERT Academic Publishing
is a trademark of
International Book Market Service Ltd., member of OmniScriptum Publishing Group
17 Meldrum Street, Beau Bassin 71504, Mauritius

Printed at: see last page
ISBN: 978-620-0-50709-9

INTRODUCTION

1.1 Drug delivery systems

Drug delivery is the method or process of administering a pharmaceutical compound to achieve a therapeutic effect in humans or animals. For the treatment of human diseases, nasal and pulmonary routes of drug delivery are gaining more importance as these routes provides promising alternatives to parenteral drug delivery particularly for peptide and protein therapeutics. For effective drug delivery systems have been tried and formulated for nasal and pulmonary drug delivery. A variety of delivery system include liposomes, proliposomes, microspheres, gels, prodrugs, nanoparticles system etc. Nanoparticles composed of biodegradable polymers show assurance in fulfilling the stringent requirements placed on these delivery systems, such as ability to be transferred into an aerosol, stability against forces generated during aerosolization, biocompatibility, targeting of specific sites or cell populations in the lung, release of the drug in a predetermined manner, and degradation within an acceptable period of time [1].

Development of new drug molecule is expensive and time consuming. Improving safety efficacy ratio of "old" drugs has been attempted using different methods such as individualizing drug therapy, dose titration, and therapeutic drug monitoring. Delivering drug at controlled rate, slow delivery, targeted delivery are other very attractive methods and have been pursued vigorously. It is interesting to note that considerable work and many publications from USA, Europe are authored by Indian researchers [2-3].

Numerous animal and human investigations have provided an increased understanding of the pharmacokinetic and pharmacodynamic principles that govern the action and disposition of potent opioid analgesics, inhalation anesthetic agents, sedative/hypnotics, and muscle relaxants. These studies suggest that skin and buccal and nasal mucous membranes may have use as alternate routes of analgesic and anesthetic delivery. Similar developments with other compounds have produced a plethora of new devices, concepts, and techniques that have together been termed controlled-release technology (CRT). Some examples of CRTs are transdermal and transmucosal controlled-release delivery systems, nasal and buccal aerosol sprays, drug-impregnated lozenges, encapsulated cells, oral soft gels, iontophoretic devices to administer drugs through skin, and a variety of programmable, implanted drug-delivery devices. There are a number of factors stimulating interest in the development of these new devices, concepts, and techniques. Conventional drug administration methods, while widely utilized, have many problems that may be potentially overcome by these methods. Equally important, these advances may appear attractive relative to the costs of new drug development. Rising research and development costs, alternative investment opportunities for drug firms, fewer firms conducting pharmaceutical research, and erosion of effective patent life have resulted in a decline in the introduction of new chemical entities since the late 1950s. Bringing a new drug through discovery, clinical testing, development, and regulatory approval is currently estimated to take a decade and cost well over $ 120 million. Novel drug delivery systems may account for as much as 40% of US marketed drug products by 2000 [4-6]

Fig. 1.1: Classification of drug delivery system

1.2 Conventional drug delivery

Conventional drug delivery involves the formulation of the drug into a suitable form, such as a compressed tablet for oral administration or a solution for intravenous administration. These dosage forms have been found to have serious limitations in terms of higher dosage required, lower effectiveness, toxicity and adverse side effects. New drug delivery systems have been developed or are being developed to overcome the limitation of the conventional drug delivery systems to meet the need of the healthcare profession.

These systems can be characterized as controlled drug release systems and targeted drug delivery systems.

The therapeutic benefits of these new systems include: [7]

- Increased efficacy of the drug
- Site specific delivery
- Decreased toxicity/side effects

2

- Increased convenience
- Viable treatments for previously incurable diseases
- Potential for prophylactic applications
- Better patient compliance.

Example of Conventional drug delivery

- Tablets
- capsules
- suspensions
- emulsions
- lotions
- Gels

1.3 Novel drug delivery systems

Novel drug delivery systems are designed to achieve a continuous delivery of drugs at predictable and reproducible kinetics over an extended period of time in the circulation. The potential advantages of this concept include minimization of drug related side effects due to controlled therapeutic blood levels instead of oscillating blood levels, improved patient compliance due to reduced frequency of dosing and the reduction of the total dose of drug administered [8-9].

Hence, the combination of both sustained release and control release properties in a delivery system would further enhance therapeutic efficacy.

1.3.1 Advantages of novel drug delivery system

Followings are advantages of novel drug delivery system [10-12].

1. Protection from physical and chemical degradation.

2. Sustained delivery.

3. Improved tissue macrophages distribution.

4. Enhancement of stability.

5. Enhancement of pharmacological activity.

6. Protection from toxicity.

7. Increased bioavailability.

8. Enhancement of solubility.

1.4 Nanoparticles

Nanoparticles are solid colloidal particles ranging from 10 to 1000 nm (1.0 μm), in which the active drug or biologically active material are dissolved, entrapped.[13]

Goal of nanotechnology is same as that of medicine: to diagnose as accurately and early as possible and to treat as effectively as possible without any side effects using controlled and targeted drug delivery approach [14].

Nanoparticles made from solid lipids are attracting major attention as novel colloidal drug carrier for intravenous applications as they have been proposed as an alternative particulate carrier system. The system consists of spherical solid lipid particles in the nanometer ranges, which are dispersed in water or in aqueous surfactant solution. Generally, they are made of solid hydrophobic core having a monolayer of phospholipids coating. The solid core contains the drug dissolved or dispersed in the solid high melting fat matrix. The hydrophobic chains of phospholipids are embedded in the fat matrix. They have potential to carry lipophilic or hydrophilic drugs or diagnostics [15

]

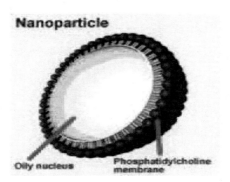

Fig. 1.2: Structure of Nanoparticle

1.4.1 Nanoparticles are classified as:-

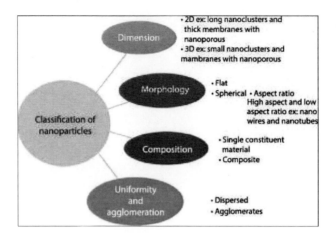

Fig. 1.3: Classification of nanoparticles [16]

The major concern with the metallic and polymeric nanoparticles is the toxic effects of metals and polymers used in the preparation of nanoparticles. As the lipids used in the preparation are categorized as GRAS (Generally Recognised as Safe) substances [17-18].

Lipid Nanoparticles can be subdivided into two types: –

- Solid Lipid Nanoparticles (SLN)
- Nanostructured Lipid Carriers (NLC)

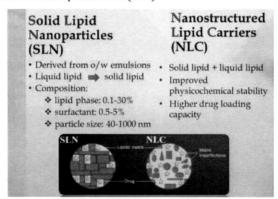

Fig. 1.4: Difference between the two basic types of lipid nanoparticles

1.5 Solid Lipid Nanoparticles (Slns)

Solid lipid nanoparticles (SLN) introduced in 1991 represent an alternative carrier system to tradition colloidal carriers such as - emulsions, liposomes and polymeric micro – and nanoparticles [19].

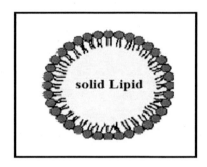

Fig 1.5: Structure of solid lipid nanoparticle

SLN are sub-micron colloidal carriers ranging from 50 to 1000 nm, which are composed of physiological lipid, dispersed in water or in aqueous surfactant solution. Sln offer unique properties such as small size, large surface area, high drug loading and the interaction of phases at the interface and are attractive for their potential to improve performance of pharmaceuticals. [20]

In order to overcome the disadvantages associated with the liquid state of the oil droplets, the liquid lipid was replaced by a solid lipid, which eventually transformed into solid lipid nanoparticles.

1.5.1 The reasons for choice lipid based system are: –

1. Lipids enhance oral bioavailability and reduce plasma profile variability.
2. Better characterization of lipoid excipients.
3. An improved ability to address the key issues of technology transfer and manufacture scale-up [21-22].

1.5.2 Aims of solid lipid nanoparticles: -

• Possibility of controlled drug release
• Increased drug stability.
• High drug pay load.
• No bio-toxicity of the carrier.

• Avoidance of organic solvents.

• Incorporation of lipophilic and hydrophilic drugs [23].

1.5.3 Advantages and Disadvantages of solid lipid nanoparticle [24-26]

S. No.	Advantages	Disadvantages
1	Control and / or target drug release	Particle growth.
2	Excellent biocompatibility	Unpredictable gelation tendency.
3	Improve stability of pharmaceuticals	Unexpected dynamics of polymeric transitions [27]
4	High and enhanced drug content	Poor drug loading capacity.
5	Easy to scale up and sterilize	Drug expulsion after polymeric transition during storage.
6	Better control over release kinetics of encapsulated compounds	Relatively high-water content of the dispersions (70-99.9%).[28]
7	Enhanced bioavailability of entrapped bioactive compounds	Molecule development
8	Much easier to manufacture than biopolymeric nanoparticles	Eccentric gelation propensity
9	Very high long-term stability	Unforeseen motion of polymeric transition [29]
10	Application flexibility [30]	

1.5.4 Composition of solid lipid nanoparticles:-

• **LIPIDS :-**

The lipid, itself, is the main ingredient of lipid nanoparticles that influence their drug loading capacity, their stability and the sustained release behavior of the formulations. [31]

Selection criteria for lipids:

Important point to be considered in the selection of drug carrier system (lipid) is its loading capacity and also the intended use.[32]

➢ Lipids that form highly crystalline particles with a perfect lattice cause drug expulsion.

➤ More complex lipids containing fatty acids of different chain length form less perfect crystals with many imperfections. These imperfections provide the space to accommodate the drugs.

Table No. 1.1: Excipients used for the preparation of solid lipid nanoparticles [33-34]

LIPIDS	Surfactants and Co-Surfactants
Triacylglycerols: Tricaprin Trilaurin Trimyristin Tripalmitin ,Tristearin	**Phospholipids:** Soy lecithin Egg lecithin Phosphatidylcholine
Acylglycerols: Glycerol monostearate Glycerol behenate Glycerol palmitostearate	**Ethylene oxide/propylene oxide copolymers:** Poloxamer 188 Poloxamer 182 Poloxamer 407 Poloxamine 908
Fatty acids: Stearic acid Palmitic acid Decanoic acid Behenic acid	**Sorbitan ethylene oxide/propylene oxide copolymers:** Polysorbate 20 Polysorbate 60 Polysorbate 80
Waxes: Cetyl palmitate	**Alkylaryl polyether alcohol polymers:** Tyloxapol
Cyclic complexes: Cyclodextrin	**Bile salts:** Sodium cholate Sodium glycocholate Sodium taurocholate Sodium taurodeoxycholate

	Taurocholic acid sodium salt
Hard fat types:	**Alcohols:**
Witepsol W 35	Ethanol
Witepsol H 35	Butanol

Other excipients [35]

Cryoprotectants	Trehalose, mannose mannitol, polyvinyl, pyrolidone, glucose, maltose, lactose, glycine, gelatin, etc.
Charge modifiers	Stearylamine, diacetyl phosphate, dipalmitoyl phosphatidyl choline (DPPC), dimyristoyl phosphatidyl glycerol (DMPG)
Stealthing agents (agents for improving circulation time)	Poloxamer, polyethylene glycol

1.5.5. Challenges for formulation and delivery:-

Problems frequently occurring with many drugs are: [36]

➢ Poor solubility

➢ Insufficient in vitro stability (shelf life)

➢ Too low bioavailability

➢ Too short in vivo stability (half-life)

➢ Strong side effect

➢ Need for targeted delivery

➢ Regulatory issues/hurdles

1.5.6 Methods of preparation of solid lipid nanoparticles :-

SLNs are prepared from lipid, emulsifier and water/solvent by using different methods are following [37-38]:-

1. High pressure homogenization

   A. Hot homogenization

   B. Cold homogenization

2. Ultrasonication/high speed homogenization

A. Probe ultrasonication

B. Bath ultrasonication

3. Solvent evaporation method

4. Solvent emulsification-diffusion method

5. Supercritical fluid method

6. Microemulsion based method

7. Spray drying method

8. Double emulsion method

9. Precipitation technique

10. Film-ultrasound dispersion

1. High pressure homogenization

It is a reliable and powerful technique, which is used for the production of SLNs. High pressure homogenizers push a liquid with high pressure (100–2000 bar) through a narrow gap (in the range of a few microns). The fluid accelerates on a very short distance to very high velocity (over 1000 Km/h). Very high shear stress and cavitation forces disrupt the particles down to the submicron range. Generally 5-10% lipid content is used but up to 40% lipid content has also been investigated [39].

Types of High pressure homogenization are hot homogenization and cold homogenization, work on the same concept of mixing the drug in bulk of lipid melt [40-41].

A. Hot homogenization:

Hot homogenization is carried out at temperatures above the melting point of the lipid and can therefore be regarded as the homogenization of an emulsion, proceses are shown in fig. 1.6

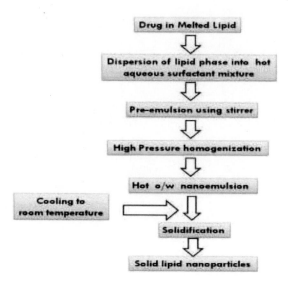

Fig. 1.6: Solid lipid nanoparticles preparation by hot homogenization process

B. Cold homogenization:

Cold homogenization has been developed to overcome various problems associated with hot Homogenization such as: Temperature-induced drug degradation, drug distribution into the aqueous phase during homogenization, and the proceses are shown in fig. 1.7

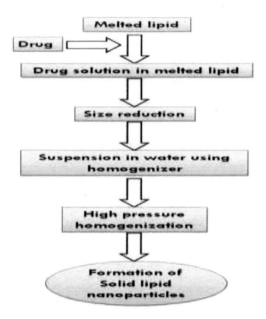

Fig 1.7: Solid lipid nanoparticles preparation by cold homogenization process

Advantages:-

- Low capital cost.

Disadvantages:-

- Energy intensive process.
- Demonstrated at lab scale biomolecule damage.[42]

2. Ultrasonication/high speed homogenization:

SLNs are also prepared by ultrasonication or high speed homogenization techniques. For smaller particle size combination of both ultrasonication and high speed homogenization is required [43].

Advantages:-

- Reduced shear stress.

Disadvantages:-

- Physical instability like particle growth upon storage.

3. Solvent evaporation:

SLNs can also prepared by solvent evaporation method. The lipophilic material is dissolved in a water-immiscible organic solvent (e.g. cyclohexane) that is emulsified in an aqueous phase. Upon evaporation of the solvent, nanoparticles dispersion is formed by precipitation of the lipid in the aqueous medium by giving the nanoparticles of 25 nm mean size. The solution was emulsified in an aqueous phase by high pressure homogenization. The organic solvent was removed from the emulsion by evaporation under reduced pressure (40–60 mbar) [44].

Advantages:-

- Scalable.
- Continuous process.
- Commercially demonstrated.

Disadvantages:-

- Extremely energy intensive process.
- Polydisperse distributions.

4. Solvent emulsification-diffusion method

The particles with average diameters of 30-100 nm can be obtained by this technique. Voidance of heat during the preparation is the most important advantage of this technique.

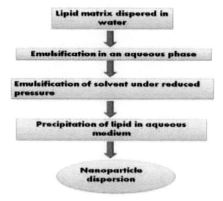

Fig 1.8: Systematic representation for emulsification-diffusion method

5. Supercritical fluid method:

There are several variation in this platform technology for powder and nanoparticle preparation. SLN can be prepared by the rapid expansion of supercritical carbon dioxide solution method. [45]

Advantages:-

- Avoid the use of solvents.
- Particles are obtained as a dry powder, instead of suspensions.
- Mild pressure and temperature conditions.
- Carbon dioxide solution is the good choice as a solvent for this method.

6. Microemulsion based method:

This method is based on the dilution of microemulsions. As micro-emulsions are two-phase systems composed of an inner and outer phase (e.g. o/w microemulsions). This process are shown in fig 1.9[46]

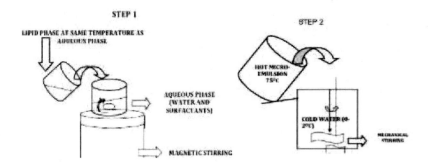

Fig 1.9: Microemulsion method

Advantages

- Low mechanical energy input.
- Theoretical stability.

Disadvantages

- Extremely sensitive to change.
- Labor intensive formulation work.
- Low nanoparticle concentrations.

7. Spray drying method:

It is an alternative technique to the lyophilization process. This recommends the use of lipid with melting point more than 70°C. The best results were obtained with SLN concentration of 1% in a solution of trehalose in water or 20% trehalose in ethanol-water mixture.[47]

8. Double emulsion method:

Here the drug is encapsulated with a stabilizer to prevent the partitioning of drug in to external water phase during solvent evaporation in the external water phase of w/o/w double emulsion.[48]

9. Precipitation method:

The glycerides are dissolved in an organic solvent (e.g. chloroform) and the solution will be emulsified in an aqueous phase. After evaporation of the organic solvent the lipid will be precipitated forming nanoparticles.

10. Film-ultrasound dispersion:

The lipid and the drug were put into suitable organic solutions, after decompression, rotation and evaporation of the organic solutions, a lipid film is formed, then the aqueous solution which includes the emulsions was added. Using the ultrasound with the probe to diffuser at last, the SLN with the little and uniform particle size is formed.

Secondary Production Steps:-

Freeze drying:

Lyophilization is a promising way to increase the chemical and physical stability over extended periods of time. Lyophilization had been required to achieve long term stability for a product containing hydrolysable drugs or a suitable product for per-oral administration. Transformation into the solid state would prevent the Oswald ripening and avoid hydrolytic reactions.

In case of freeze drying of the product, all the lipid matrices used, form larger solid lipid nanoparticles with a wider size distribution due to presence of aggregates between the nanoparticles. The conditions of the freeze drying process and the removal of water promote the aggregation among SLNs. An adequate amount of cryoprotectant can protect the aggregation of solid lipid nanoparticles during the freeze drying process.

Sterilization:

Sterilization of the nanoparticles is desirable for parenteral administration and autoclaving which is applicable to formulations containing heat-resistant drugs. Effects of sterilization on particle size have been investigated and it was found to cause a distinct increase in particle size.

Spray drying:

Spray drying might be an alternative procedure to lyophilization in order to transform an aqueous SLN dispersion into a dry product. This method has been used scarcely for SLN formulation, although spray drying is cheaper as compared to lyophilization. The lipids with melting points at temperature >70°C had been recommended for spray drying.

1.5.7 Storage stability of SLN:

The physical properties of SLN's during prolonged storage can be determined by monitoring changes in zeta potential, particle size, drug content, appearance and viscosity as the function of time. External parameters such as temperature and light appear to be of primary importance for long term stability. The zeta potential should be in between -100 to + 100 mV for a dispersion to remain physically stable. [49]

4°C - Most favorable storage temperature.

20°C - Long term storage did not result in drug loaded SLN aggregation or loss of drug.

50°C - A rapid growth of particle size is observed [50]

1.5.8 Routes of administration and their biodistribution: - The *in vivo* behavior of the SLN particles will mainly depend on the following points: [51-53]

Administration route

Interactions of the SLN with the biological surroundings including: distribution processes (adsorption of biological material on the particle surface and desorption of SLN components into to biological surroundings) and enzymatic processes. Various administration routes are:

1. Parenteral administration

Peptide and proteins drugs are usually available for parenteral use in the market. Since their conventional oral administration is not possible due to enzymatic degradation in GI tract. Parenteral application of SLN reduces the possible side effects of drug incorporated with the increased bioavailability. These systems are very suitable for drug targeting.

2. Oral administration

Controlled release behavior of SLNs is reported to enable the bypass of gastric and intestinal degradation of the encapsulated drug, and their possible uptake and transport through the intestinal mucosa. However, the assessment of the stability of colloidal carriers in GI fluids is essential in order to predict their suitability for oral administration.

3. Rectal administration

When rapid pharmacological effect is required, in some circumstances, parenteral or rectal administration is preferred. This route is used for pediatric patients due to easy application.

4. Nasal administration

Nasal route is preferred due to its fast absorption and rapid onset of drug action also avoiding degradation of labile drugs in the GIT and insufficient transport across epithelial cell layers.

5. Respiratory delivery

Nebulisation of solid lipid particles carrying anti-tubercular drugs, anti-asthmatic drugs and anti-cancer was observed to be successful in improving drug bioavailability and reducing the dosing frequency for better management of pulmonary action.

6. Ocular administration

Biocompatibility and muco-adhesive properties of SLN improve their interaction with ocular mucosa and prolong corneal residence time of the drug, with the aim of ocular drug targeting.

7. Topical administration

SLN are very attractive colloidal carrier systems for skin applications due to their various desirable effects on skin besides the characteristics of a colloidal carrier system. They are well suited for use on damaged or inflamed skin because they are based on non-irritant and non-toxic lipids.

1.5.9 Drug incorporation models of SLN:-

Factors affecting loading capacity of a drug in lipid are:

1. Solubility of drug in lipid melt.

2. Miscibility of drug melt and lipid melt.

3. Chemical and physical structure of solid matrix lipid.

4. Polymorphic state of lipid material. [54]

There are three drug incorporation models which describe drug release from SLN as shown in fig.1.10:

A) Homogenous matrix model

B) Drug enriched shell with lipid core

C) Drug enriched core with lipid shell [55]

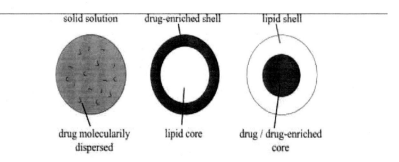

Fig 1.10: Three Models of Drug- Incorporation into a Solid Lipid Nanoparticle

Table No. 1.2: Homogeneous Matrix Model, Drug – Enriched Core Model, Drug – Enriched Shell Model

Solid solution model	Core-shell model (drug-enriched shell)	Core-shell model enriched core)
Formation of this model in cold homogenization technique	Formation of this model in hot homogenization technique	Dispersion cooling leads to a super saturation of the drug which is dissolved in the lipid.
Using no drug-solubilizing surfactant	Formation of lipid core at recrystallization temperature of lipid	Precipitation of drug in melted lipid
Drug dispersed in lipid	Cooling of the obtained	Finally, further cooling lead

18

matrix	dispersion leads to repartitioning of the drug to the lipid phase	to recrystallization of the lipid
There is a strong interaction between lipid and drug	Concentration of drug in surrounding membrane	Formation of drug-enriched core

1.5.10 Mechanism of drug release through solid lipid nanoparticles:-

In vitro and *ex vivo* **methods for the assessment of drug release from SLN** [56-57]

A large number of drugs including very hydrophilic molecules have been postulated to be incorporated into SLN.

Various methods used to study the *in vitro* release of the drug are:-

- Side by side diffusion cells with artificial or biological membrane [58].
- Dialysis bag diffusion technique.
- Reverse dialysis bag technique.
- Agitation followed by ultracentrifugation or centrifugal ultra filtration.

In vitro drug release

Dialysis tubing

In vitro drug release could be achieved using dialysis tubing. The solid lipid nanoparticle dispersion is placed in pre - washed dialysis tubing which can be hermetically sealed. The dialysis sac then dialyzed against a suitable dissolution medium at room temperature; the samples are withdrawn from the dissolution medium at suitable intervals, centrifuged and analyzed for the drug content using a suitable analytical method. [59]

Ex vivo model for determining permeability across the gut

Ahlin et al. demonstrated the passage of enalaprilat SLN's across rat jejunum. In short the rat jejunum (20 – 30 cm distal from the pyloric sphincter) was excised from the rats after sacrificing the animal used for the study. Qing Zhi Lu et al. excised 10 cm long segments of duodenum (1 cm distal to pyloric sphincter); jejunum (15 cm to pyloric sphincter), ileum (20 cm proximal to cecum) and colon (2 cm distal to cecum) were immediately cannulated and ligated on both sides used for their permeability studies. [60]

1.5.11 Principle of Drug Release from SLN:

The general standards of medication discharge from lipid nanoparticles are as per the following: [61].

1. Higher surface territory because of little molecule measure in nanometer extent gives higher medication discharge.

2. Slow medication discharge can be accomplished when the medication is homogenously scattered in the lipid framework. It depends on sort and medication entanglement model of SLN.

3. Crystallization conduct of the lipid carrier and high portability of the medication lead to quick medication discharge.

4. Fast initial drug release in the first 5 min in the drug –enriched shell model as a result of the outer layer of particle due to larger surface area of drug depositon on the particle surface.

5. The type of surfactant and its concentration, which will interact with the outer shell and affect its structure, should be noted as the outer factor which is important, because a low surfactant concentration leads to a minimal burst and prolonged drug release.

6. The particle size affect drug release rate directly depends on various parameters such as composition of SLN formulation (such as surfactant, structural properties of lipid, drug) production method and conditions (such as production time, equipment, sterilization and lyophilization [62].

Fate of SLN after oral administration:-

The oral route continues to be a challenge as well as the most attractive way to administer drugs because of its unquestionable commercial potential. Incorporation of drugs into lipid nanoparticles opens the perspective of enhanced and / or less variable bioavailability and prolonged plasma levels. While these systems may provide the greatest flexibility in the modulation of the drug release profile within GIT and provide protection against chemical degradation for labile drug molecules (Peptide drugs) [63-65].

1.5.12 Characterization parameters:-

Physiochemical Characterization of SLNs:

1. Particle Size and Shape

SLNs are submicron sized, particle size and shape is determined by:

a) Photon Correlation Spectroscopy

It is an established method which is based on dynamic scattering of laser light due to Brownian motion of particlesin solution/suspension. This method is suitable for the measurement of particles in the range of 3 nm to 3 mm. The PCS device consists of laser source, a sample cell (temperature controlled) and a detector. Photomultiplier is used as detector to detect the scattered light. The PCS diameter is based on the intensity of the light scattering from the particles [66].

b) Electron Microscopy

Electron Microscopy methods such as Scanning Electron Microscopy (SEM) and Transmission Electron Microscopy (TEM) are used to measure the physical characterization like overall shape and morphology of lipid nanoparticles. It permits the determination of particle size and distributions.SEM uses electrons transmitted from the surface of the sample while TEM uses electrons transmitted through the sample. TEM has a smaller size limit of detection [67].

2. Measurement of zeta potential

Zeta potential is used to measure the charge on the particles. It allows prediction about the storage stability of colloidal dispersion because of repulsion between particles. Malvern Zetasizer is most widely used instrument for measurement of Zeta potential. A zeta potential measurement can also be helpful in designing particles with reduced RES uptake. Zeta potential below -25 mV and above + 25mV are required for full electrostatic stabilization of the formulation [68].

3. Determination of Incorporated Drug

Amount of drug incorporated in SLNs influences the release characteristics; hence it is very important to measure the amount of incorporated drug. The amount of drug encapsulated per unit weight of nanoparticles is determined after separation of the free drug and solid lipids from the aqueous medium by ultracentrifugation,

centrifugation filtration or gel permeation chromatography. The drug can be assayed by standard analytical technique such as spectroscopy and HPLC methods.

4. Measurement of degree of crystallinity and lipid modification

Thermodynamic stability and lipid packing density increase while drug incorporation rates decrease in the following order:

Super cooled melt < α-modification < β'-modification < β-modification.

Due to the small size of the particles and the presence of emulsifiers, lipid crystallization and modification changes might be highly retarded. Differential scanning calorimetry (DSC) & X-ray scattering are used to investigate the status of the lipid. DSC uses the fact that different lipid modifications possess different melting points and melting enthalpies. By means of X-ray scattering it is possible to assess the length of the long and short spacing of the lipid lattice. It is highly recommended to measure changes of the SLN dispersion because solvent removal will lead to modifications.

Table No. 1.3: Characterization Parameters

S. No.	Parameters	Importance	Methods
1.	Size and Shape	Determine skin penetration	Photon correlation spectroscopy, Scanning electron microscopy (SEM), Transmission electron microscopy (TEM)
2.	Zeta potential	Stability of particles	Zeta potentiometer, Laser droplet anemometry
3.	Entrapment Efficiency	Suitability of method	Ultracentrifugation
4.	Drug content	Important in deciding the amount of nanoparticles preparation to be used	UV, HPLC
5.	*In-vitro* dissolution	Determine the drug release rate from particles.	Under physiologic and sink conditions.

1.5.13 Applications of SLN:-

There are several potential applications of SLNs some of which are given below: [69]

- SLN as potential new adjuvant for vaccines.
- Solid lipid nanoparticles in cancer chemotherapy.
    - SLN as targeted carrier for anticancer drug to solid tumor.
    - SLN in breast cancer and lymph node metastases.
- Solid lipid nanoparticles for delivering peptides and proteins.

- Solid lipid nanoparticles for targeted brain drug delivery.
- Solid lipid nanoparticles for parasitic diseases.
- Solid lipid nanoparticles for ultrasonic drug and gene delivery.
- SLN applications for improved delivery of antiretroviral drugs to the brain.
- SLN applied to the treatment of malaria.
- Targeted delivery of solid lipid nanoparticles for the treatment of lung diseases.
- Solid lipid nanoparticles in tuberculosis disease.
- Transfection agent. SLN in cosmetic and dermatological preparations.
- Solid lipid nanoparticles for lymphatic targeting.
- SLN for potential agriculture applications.

LITERATURE REVIEW

Amaldoss M J Newton et al (2019) focuses on the recently exposed potential of SLNs in cosmetics, methods of preparation, characterization, in vitro studies, stability, toxicity, and applications for the skin and in other drug delivery targets.[70]

Fakhar ud Din et al (2019) developed ezetimibe-loaded solid lipid nanoparticles (SLNs) and compared them with marketed product and drug suspension for dissolution and bioavailability. Ezetimibe-loaded SLNs were fabricated using high pressure homogeniser (HPH). The content of SLNs were (drug, solid lipid and surfactant; 50/300/25 mg/ml of distilled water). They were characterized through particle size, poly dispersive index (PDI), zeta potential and entrapment efficiency (EE). Moreover, dynamic scattering calorimetry (DSC) and powder x-ray diffraction (PXRD) were also performed.[71]

AldemarGordillo-Galeano et al (2018) focused on the development of different formulations using a wide variety of excipients and active molecules. However, there is no consensus on the structure of the particles in these colloidal systems, in this review the most common materials and preparation methods to obtain lipid particles are presented. Also, the particle characteristics, including the shape, size and size distribution, zeta potential, drug load capacity and drug entrapment efficiency are synthesized and analyzed with the help of scientometrics tools [72]

HuaixiangTian et al (2018) were prepared Citral-loaded solid lipid nanoparticles (citral-SLNs) via a high-pressure homogenization method, using glyceryl monostearate (GMS) as the solid lipid and a mixture of Tween 80 (T-80) and Span 80 (S-80) at a weight ratio of 1:1 as the surfactant. The microstructure and properties of the citral-SLNs were characterized by dynamic light scattering (DLS), scanning electron microscopy (SEM), differential scanning calorimetry (DSC), Fourier-transform infrared spectroscopy (FTIR), X-ray diffraction (XRD) and thermal gravimetric analysis (TGA). The chemical stability of citral in the citral-SLNs was analyzed by solid-phase microextraction gas chromatography (SPME-GC). The GC results showed that 67.0% of the citral remained in the citral-SLN suspensions after 12 days, while only 8.22% remained in the control. Therefore, the encapsulation of citral in the solid lipid can enhance its stability in acidic surroundings.[73]

Christos Tapeinos et al (2017) studied of active and passive targeting SLNs and NLCs for the treatment of glioblastoma multiforme and of other brain cancers, as well as for the treatment of neurodegenerative diseases is also carried out. Finally, a brief description of the advantages, the disadvantages, and the future perspectives in the use of these nanocarriers is reported, aiming at giving an insight of the limitations that have to be overcome in order to result in a delivery system with high therapeutic efficacy and without the limitations of the existing nano-systems. [74]

Chih-Hung Lin et al (2017) highlighted the recent progress in the development of SLNs for disease treatment, for cancers, central nervous system-related disorders, cardiovascular-related diseases, infection, diabetes, and osteoporosis. They systematically introduce the concepts and amelioration mechanisms of the nanomedical techniques for drug- and natural compound-loaded SLNs. [75]

Leila Azhar Shekoufeh Bahari et al (2016) have shown numerous merits in drug delivery. Size is the most important index in a nanocarrier affecting its drug delivery efficiency. The influence of preparation conditions and type of lipidic components on the size of SLN in comparable states seems to be interesting for researchers who investigate these types of carriers. They highlight the results of SLN and NLC particle size and size distribution comparisons. [76]

Mlgorzata Geszke -Moritz et al (2016) studied briefly reviews up-to-date developments in solid lipid nanoparticles (SLNs) as effective nanocolloidal system for drug delivery. It also summarizes SLNs in terms of their preparation, surface modification and properties. [77]

Neda Naseri et al (2015) was focused on features, structure and innovation of Lipid nanoparticles (LNPs) and presents a wide discussion about preparation methods, advantages, disadvantages and applications of Lipid nanoparticles (LNPs) by focusing on SLNs and NLCs. [78]

YangchaoLuo et al (2015) studied a series of SLN was prepared to investigate the effects of surfactant/cosurfactant and chitosan coating on their physicochemical properties as well as cellular uptake. SLN was prepared from Compritol 888 ATO using a low-energy method combining the solvent-diffusion and hot homogenization technique. Poloxamer 188 and polyethylene glycol (PEG) were effective emulsifiers to produce SLN with better physicochemical properties than SLN control. Overall, chitosan-coated SLN was superior to other formulations and held promising features for its application as a potential oral drug delivery system for hydrophobic drugs.[79]

Vinay Yadav et al (2014) discussed the preparation method, characterization, route of administration of SLNs, advantages, different preparation method which are suitable for large scale production and application of SLNs. Analytical techniques for characterization of SLNs like photon correlation spectroscopy, scanning electron microscopy, different scanning colorimetry are highlighted [80]

KinamPark (2014) was largely focused on studying nanoparticle formulations, and it will continue playing a leading role in the next generation. The best path towards a productive 3rd generation of drug delivery technology requires an honest, open dialog without any preconceived ideas of the past. The drug delivery field needs to take a bold approach to designing future drug delivery formulations primarily based on today's necessities, to produce the necessary innovations. The JCR provides a forum for sharing the new ideas that will shape the 3rd generation of drug delivery technology.[81]

Neha Yadav et al (2013) gives an overview about the potential advantages and also the disadvantages of solid lipid nanoparticles, the excipients and all the different methods involved in their production including the membrane contractor method. Aspects of SLN stability and the influence of various excipients (used in SLN production) on stability with other secondary steps involved in their stabilization like freeze drying, spray drying etc. Problems associated with SLN production and instrumental techniques used in production are thoroughly discussed.[82]

Jeetendra SinghNegi et al (2013) were prepared Solid lipid nanoparticles (SLNs) of poor orally bioavailable drug lopinavir using hot self nano-emulsification (SNE) technique. Hot isotropic mixture of stearic acid, poloxamer and polyethylene glycol was spontaneously self nano-emulsify in hot water and SLNs were formed with subsequent rapid cooling. Self nano-emulsification ability of stearic acid, poloxamer and polyethylene glycol mixture was assessed by ternary phase diagram study. Results indicate that SLNs of higher fatty acids can be successfully prepared by hot SNE technique.[83]

WolfgangMehnert et al (2012) presents an overview about the selection of the ingredients, different ways of SLN production and SLN applications. Aspects of SLN stability and possibilities of SLN stabilization by lyophilization and spray drying are discussed. Special attention is paid to the relation between drug incorporation and the complexity of SLN dispersions, which includes the presence of alternative colloidal structures (liposomes, micelles, drug nanosuspensions, mixed micelles, liquid crystals) and the physical state of the lipid (supercooled melts, different lipid modifications). [84] **Akanksha Garud et al (2012)** focuses on the utility of SLN in terms of their advantages, production methodology, characterization and applications. If properly investigated, SLNs may open new vistas in therapy of complex diseases.[85]

Surajit Das et al (2011) prepared solid lipid nanoparticles (SLNs) of a hydrophobic drug, tretinoin, by emulsification–ultrasonication method. Solubility of tretinoin in the solid lipids was examined. Effects of process variables were investigated on particle size, polydispersity index (PI), zeta potential (ZP), drug encapsulation efficiency (EE), and drug loading (L) of the SLNs. Shape and surface morphology of the SLNs were investigated by cryogenic field emission scanning electron microscopy (cryo-FESEM). Complete encapsulation of drug in the nanoparticles was checked by cross-polarized light microscopy and differential scanning calorimetry (DSC). Crystallinity of the formulation was analyzed by DSC and powder X-ray diffraction (PXRD). In addition, drug release and stability studies were also performed. [86]

Diego Delgado et al (2011) evaluated the effect of protamine on the transfection capacity of solid lipid nanoparticles (SLNs) by correlating it to the internalization mechanisms and intracellular trafficking of the vectors. Vectors were prepared with SLN, DNA, and protamine. ARPE-19 and HEK-293 cells were used for the evaluation of the formulations. [87]

Sanju Dhawanet al (2010) formulated solid lipid nanoparticles (SLNs) of quercetin, a natural flavonoid with established antioxidant activity, for intravenous administration in order to improve its permeation across the blood–brain barrier into the CNS, and eventually to improve the therapeutic efficacy of this molecule in Alzheimer's disease. [88]

Ali Seyfoddin et al (2010) detailed the various production, characterization, sterilization, and stabilization techniques for SLNs. *In-vitro* and *in-vivo* methods to study the drug release profile of SLNs have been explained. Special attention has been given to the nature of lipids and surfactants commonly used for SLN production. A summary of previous studies involving the use of SLNs in ocular drug delivery is provided, along with a critical evaluation of SLNs as a potential ocular delivery system. [89]

Ziyaur Rahman et al (2010) was evaluated compositional variations and their interaction of the solid lipid nanoparticle (SLN) formulation of risperidone using response surface methodology of design of experiment (DOE) and subsequently, characterize the SLN by non-destructive methods of analysis. [90]

Hou Li Li et al (2009) was design and characterized quercetin-loaded solid lipid nanoparticles (QT-SLNs), clarify the absorption mechanism of QT-SLNs and to evaluate the potential of using solid lipid nanoparticles (SLNs) as an oral delivery carrier for poorly water soluble drugs. QT-SLNs were prepared by an emulsification and low-temperature solidification method. [91]

Qingzhi Lv et al (2009) was developed solid lipid nanoparticles (SLNs) of penciclovir and evaluated the potential of SLNs as the carrier of penciclovir for topical delivery. Penciclovir-loaded SLNs were prepared by a double (W/O/W) emulsion technique. The SLNs presented spherical with the mean diameter of 254.9 nm. [92]

Jana Pardeike et al (2009) focusesd on lipid nanoparticles for dermal application. Production of lipid nanoparticles and final products containing lipid nanoparticles is feasible by well-established production methods. Overview of the cosmetic products currently on the market was given and the improvement of the benefit/risk ratio of the topical therapy was shown. [93]

V. Jannin et al (2008) presented the recent approaches in selecting the most appropriate lipid system(s); methods for characterization of their behavior in vitro and in vivo; and the current formulation and processing techniques to obtain various solid dosage forms. [94]

Anthony A. Attama et al (2008) were prepared solid lipid nanoparticles (SLNs) with a combination of homolipid from goat (goat fat) and phospholipid, and evaluated for diclofenac sodium (DNa) delivery to the eye using bio-engineered human cornea, produced from immortalized human corneal endothelial cells (HENC), stromal fibroblasts and epithelial cells. [95]

Indu Pal Kaur et al (2008) was discused about the barriers to CNS drug delivery, strategies to bypass the blood–brain barrier and characterization methods of SLNs and their usefulness. The proposed mechanism of uptake, methods of prolonging the plasma retention and the in vivo and in vitro methods for assessment will also be discussed in some details. [96]

Jie Liu et al (2008) studied novel nebulizer-compatible solid lipid nanoparticles (SLNs) for pulmonary drug delivery of insulin were developed by reverse micelle-double emulsion method. The influences of the amount of sodium cholate (SC) and soybean phosphatidylcholine (SPC) on the deposition properties of the nanoparticles were investigated. [97]

A. del Pozo-Rodriguez et al (2007) studied on different formulations based on SLN–DNA complexes were formulated in order to evaluate the influence of the formulation components on the "in vitro" transfection capacity. The formulations prepared at DOTAP/DNA ratios 7/1, 5/1 and 4/1 provided almost the same transfection levels (around 15% transfected cells), without significant differences between them (p > 0.05). [98]

Antonio J. Almeida et al (2007) developed in the area confirms that under optimized conditions they can be produced to incorporate hydrophobic or hydrophilic proteins and seem to fulfil the requirements for an optimum particulate carrier system. Proteins and antigens intended for therapeutic purposes may be incorporated or adsorbed onto SLN, and further administered by parenteral routes or by alternative routes such as oral, nasal and pulmonary. [99]

Paolo Blasi et al (2007) discussed the potential use of solid lipid nanoparticles for brain drug targeting purposes. The state of the art on surfactant coated poly(alkylcyanoacrylate) nanoparticles specifically designed for brain targeting is given by emphasizing the transfer of this technology to solid lipid matrices.[100]

Gisele A. Castro et al (2007) developed SLN with high encapsulation efficiency using a low surfactant/lipid ratio. Different formulations of retinoic acid-loaded SLN were prepared using glyceryl behenate as lipid matrix. The particle size, encapsulation efficiency, zeta potential and differential scanning calorimetry (DSC) were investigated. High encapsulation efficiency in SLN was obtained with addition of amines. They indicated that the utilization of amines is an interesting approach to improve the encapsulation efficiency of in SLN using a low surfactant/lipid ratio. [101]

Jie Liu et al (2007) was constructed isotretinoin-loaded SLN (IT-SLN) formulation with skin targeting for topical delivery of isotretinoin. PRECIROL ATO 5 was selected as the lipid of SLN. Tween 80 and soybean lecithin were used as the surfactants to stabilize SLN. The hot homogenization method was performed to prepare the drug-loaded SLN. [102]

Kumar A. Shah et al (2007) developed solid lipid nanoparticles (SLN) of tretinoin (TRE) with the help of facile and simple emulsification-solvent diffusion (ESD) technique and to evaluate the viability of an SLN based gel in improving topical delivery of TRE. They successfully demonstrated the feasibility of fabricating SLN of TRE by the ESD method. [103]

Maria Antonietta Casadei et al (2006) studied of ibuprofen from the freeze-dried samples were performed. The comparison among the release profiles of ibuprofen from SLN, DEX-MA hydrogel and SLN/DEX-MA-hydrogel allows to affirm that this last system, retaining about 60% of the drug after 2 h in acid medium and releasing it slowly in neutral solution, is suitable for modified delivery oral formulations.[104]

Catherine Charcosset et al (2005) investigated a new process for the preparation of SLN using a membrane contactor. The lipid phase was pressed, at a temperature above the melting point of the lipid, through the membrane pores allowing the formation of small droplets. The aqueous phase circulated inside the membrane module, and sweeps away the droplets forming at the pore outlets. SLN was formed by the following cooling of the preparation to room temperature. The advantages of this new process are its facility of use, the control of the SLN size by an appropriate choice of process parameters, and its scaling-up abilities. [105]

M.A. Schubert et al (2005) was studied on development and characterisation of surface-modified SLN for adsorptive protein loading by variation of both the lipid matrix and the emulsifier concentration in the continuous phase. [106]

Rajesh Pandey et al (2005) was planned to evaluate the chemotherapeutic potential of oral solid lipid nanoparticles (SLNs) incorporating rifampicin, isoniazid and pyrazinamide against experimental tuberculosis. The SLNs were prepared by the "emulsion solvent diffusion" technique. [107]

J.E. Kipp (2004) presented a brief introduction to the pharmaceutical technology of pure submicron drug particles in relationship to other dosage forms, and study examples was presented to underscore the potential benefits of this approach in parenteral delivery. [108]

Roberta Cavalli et al (2002) evaluated solid lipid nanoparticles (SLN) as carriers for topical ocular delivery of tobramycin (TOB). The SLN were in the colloidal size range (average diameter below 100 nm; polydispersity index below 0.2) and contained 2.5% TOB as ion-pair complex with hexadecyl phosphate. [109]

Volkhard Jenning et al (2001) described the inclusion properties of colloidal lipids and to propose incorporation mechanisms. Besides the well known methods to investigate entrapment of actives in nanoparticles such as DSC or microscopy. Based on

30

the different chemical stability of retinoids in water and in a lipid phase, a method to derive information on the distribution of the drug between SLN-lipid and the water phase was established. [110]

Da-Bing Chen et al (2001) described the development of two types of long-circulating SLNs as colloidal carriers for paclitaxel. In vitro release kinetics showed that the release was very slow, the release of paclitaxel from F68-SLN is linear, and the release of paclitaxel from Brij78-SLN followed the Weibull equation. F68-SLN and Brij78-SLN are long-circulating (t1/2b , 10.06 and 4.88 h, respectively) compared with paclitaxel injection (t1/2b , 1.36 h). [111]

Volkhard Jenning et al (2000) evaluated the potential use of solid lipid nanoparticles (SLN) in dermatology and cosmetics, glyceryl behenate SLN loaded with vitamin A (retinol and retinyl palmitate) and incorporated in a hydrogel and o/w-cream were tested with respect to their in⁻uence on drug penetration into porcine skin. [112]

C. Schwarz et al (1997) studied the protective effect of various types and concentrations of cryoprotectants (e.g. carbohydrates), freeze-thaw cycles were carried out as a pre-test. The sugar trehalose proved to be most effective in preventing particle growth during freezing and thawing and also in the freeze-drying process. [113]

Roberta Cavalli et al (1997) have been prepared solid lipid nanoparticles (SLN) from three oil-in-water microemulsions, whose internal phase was constituted of different lipid matrices. They used Diazepam as model drug to incorporate into SLN, where it was shown by calorimetric analysis to be in amorphous form. [114]

RESEARCH ENVISAGED

Most of the non-steroidal anti-inflammatory medicine and drugs used for the management of pain and inflammation have number of side effects when used for the longer time in higher doses. At the same time some medicine related to this segment have poor bioavailability issue. Such problems of these medications can be eliminated with the use of novel drug delivery systems. Oxaprozin is one of the examples, which is a potent non-steroidal anti-inflammatory drug (NSAID) and possess relatively short plasma half-life (3 to 5 hours) as compared to other oxicams. Data from preliminary clinical trials suggest that Oxaprozin is as effective as the opioid analgesics morphine, pethidine (meperidine) and tramadol in relieving postoperative pain following gynaecological or orthopaedic surgery, and as effective as other NSAIDs used postoperatively. Substantial concentrations of Oxaprozin are attained in synovial fluid, the proposed site of action in chronic inflammatory arthropathies. So it is considered equally effective as other NSAIDs in relieving symptoms of osteoarthritis, rheumatoid arthritis, ankylosing spondylitis, acute sciatica and low back pain and demonstrated as potential alternative to other NSAIDs for the management of arthritis and other painful and inflammatory conditions. Oxaprozin is available in market in the form tablet and parenteral dosage form with 4 mg, 8mg which suffers from the drawback of producing gastritis and also the daily dose of the Oxaprozin should not increase more than 16 mg. Considering the dose, plasma half life and its use, it is a potent candidate which can be developed in novel drug delivery formulations leading to reduction in associated side effects of the drug and increase in patient compliance. Hence novel drug delivery systems of the drug (oxaprozin) will be developed in this project. The Objective of the project is to develop a novel formulation SLN using oxaprozin for management of pain.

PLAN OF WORK

In the present study, it is proposed to compare various vesicular approaches for the development of an economical, controlled release and patient compliant transdermal drug delivery system for a newer NSAID. The plan of work can be outlined as follows:

1) **Literature review of research articles and patents**
2) **Selection of polymers and various ingredients**
3) **Pre-formulation studies and drug analysis**
   a. Characterization of drug sample for physicochemical attributes :- FTIR, UV
   b. Solubility profile
   c. Partition coefficient
   d. Drug excipient interaction study :- DSC, FTIR
4) **Formulation development of SLN :-** Selection of suitable formulation
5) **Optimization studies**

   a.Selection of independent variables

   b.Selection of response variables

   c.Selection of experimental design for optimization of the formulation
6) **Evaluation of batches selected for optimization studies**
7) **Selection of optimum formulation**
8) **Evaluation of formulation**
9) *In vitro* **release study**

DRUG AND EXCIPIENT PROFILE

5.1 Drug Profile

5.1.1 Oxaprozin

Oxaprozin also known as oxaprozinum, is a non steroidal anti-inflammatory drug, used to relieve the inflammation, swelling, stiffness, and joint pain associated with osteoarthritis and rheumatoid arthritis.[115]

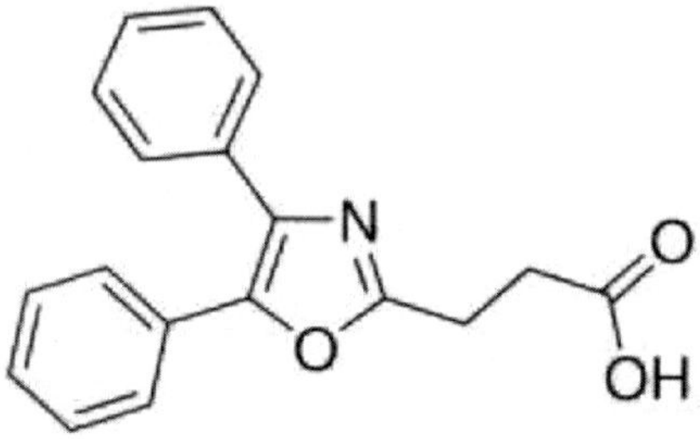

Fig. 5.1 Struture of oxaprozin

Mol. Weight: 293.322 g/mol

Chemical Formula: $C_{18}H_{15}NO_3$

IUPAC Name: 3-(4,5-diphenyl-1,3-oxazol-2-yl)propanoic acid

Pharmacology

Indication:

Used to relieve the inflammation, swelling, stiffness, and joint pain associated with rheumatoid arthritis and osteoarthritis.

Pharmacodynamics:

Oxaprozin is a nonsteroidal anti-inflammatory drug (NSAID) with analgesic and antipyretic properties. Oxaprozin is used to treat rheumatoid arthritis, osteoarthritis, dysmenorrhea, and to alleviate moderate pain. [116]

Mechanism of action:

Anti-inflammatory effects of Oxaprozin are believed to be due to inhibition of cylooxygenase in platelets which leads to the blockage of prostaglandin synthesis. Antipyretic effects may be due to action on the hypothalamus, resulting in an increased peripheral blood flow, vasodilation, and subsequent heat dissipation. Oxaprozin is a non-selective NSAID, with a cell assay system showing lower COX-2 selectivity implying higher COX-1 selectivity. This medicine may raise the chance of very bad and sometimes deadly stomach or bowel side effects like ulcers or bleeding. The risk is greater in older people. The risk is also greater in people who have had stomach or bowel ulcers or bleeding before. [117]

Absorption:

Oxaprozin is 95% absorbed after oral administration. Food may reduce the rate of absorption of oxaprozin, but the extent of absorption is unchanged. Antacids do not significantly affect the extent and rate of oxaprozin absorption.[118]

Metabolism:

Hepatic. Ester and ether glucuronide are the major conjugated metabolites of oxaprozin, and do not have significant pharmacologic activity.

Uses:

Oxaprozin is used to treat arthritis. It reduces pain, swelling, and stiffness of the joints. Oxaprozin is known as a nonsteroidal anti-inflammatory drug (NSAID).[119]

Side effects of oxaprozin

The most common side effects from oxaprozin are rash, ringing in the ears, headaches, dizziness, drowsiness, abdominal pain, nausea, diarrhea, constipation, heartburn, fluid retention, and shortness of breath.[120]

5.2 Excipients Profile

5.2.1 Lecithin

Description:

Lecithins vary greatly in their physical form, from viscous semi liquids to powders, depending upon the free fatty acid content. They may also vary in color from brown to light yellow, depending upon whether they are bleached or unbleached or on the degree of purity. When they are exposed to air, rapid oxidationoccurs, also resulting in a dark yellow or brown color.Lecithins have practically no odor. Those derived from vegetable sources have a bland or nutlike taste, similar to that of soybean oil.[121]

Nonproprietary names

USP-NF: Lecithin

Synonyms:

E322; egg lecithin; LSC 5050; LSC 6040; mixed soybean phosphatides;ovolecithin; Phosal 53 MCT; Phospholipon 100 H; ProKote LSC; soybean lecithin;soybean phospholipids; Sternpur; vegetable lecithin.

Chemical name: Lecithin

Structural formula

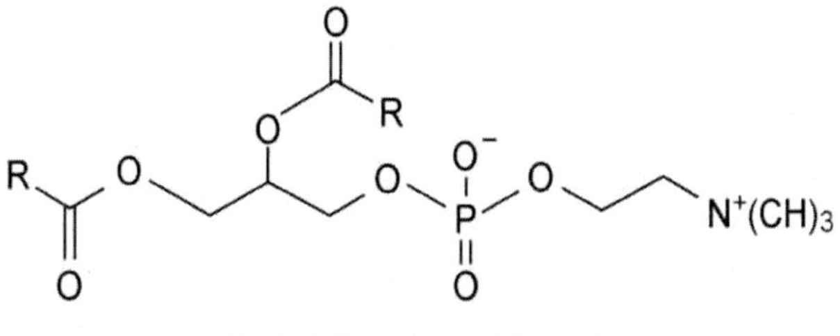

Fig 5.2: Structure of lecithin

Functional category:

Emollient; emulsifying agent; solubilizing agent.

Applications in pharmaceutical formulation or technology:

Lecithins are used in a wide variety of pharmaceutical applications. They are also used in cosmetics and food products. Lecithins are mainly used in pharmaceutical products as dispersing, emulsifying, and stabilizing agents, and are included in intramuscular and intravenous injections, parenteral nutrition formulations, and topical products such as creams and ointments. Lecithins are also used in suppository bases, to reduce thebrittleness of suppositories, and have been investigated for their absorption-enhancing properties in an intranasal insulin formulation. Lecithins are alsocommonly used as a component of enteral and parenteral nutrition formulations. There is evidence that phosphatidylcholine (a major component of lecithin) is important as a nutritional supplement to fetal and infant development. [122]

Stability and storage conditions:

Lecithins decompose at extreme pH. They are also hygroscopic and subject to microbial degradation. When heated, lecithins oxidize, darken, and decompose. Temperatures of 160–180 ^{0} C will cause degradation within 24 hours. Fluid or waxy lecithin grades should be stored at room temperature or above; temperatures below 108 ^{0} C may cause separation. All lecithin grades should be stored in well-closed containers protected from light and oxidation. Purified solid lecithin should be stored in tightly closed containers at subfreezing temperatures.

Incompatibilities:

Incompatible with esterases owing to hydrolysis.

Safety:

Lecithin is a component of cell membranes and is therefore consumed as a normal part of the diet. Although excessive consumption may be harmful, it is highly biocompatible and oral doses of up to 80 g daily have been used therapeutically in the treatment of tardive dyskinesia. When used in topical formulations, lecithin is generally regarded as a nonirritant and nonsensitizing material. The Cosmetic Ingredients Review Expert Panel (CIR) has reviewed lecithin and issued a tentative report revising the safe concentration of the material from 1.95% to 15.0% in rinse-off and leave-in products. They note, however, that there are insufficient data to rule on products that are likely to be inhaled.

Handling precautions:

Observe normal precautions appropriate to the circumstances and quantity of material handled. Lecithins may be irritant to the eyes; eye protection and gloves are recommended.

5.2.2 Stearic acid

Stearic Acid is a saturated long-chain fatty acid with an 18-carbon backbone. Stearic acid is found in various animal and plant fats, and is a major component of cocoa butter and shea butter.

Stearic acid, also called octadecanoic acid, is one of the useful types of saturated fatty acids that comes from many animal and vegetable fats and oils. It is a waxy solid, and its chemical formula is $CH_3(CH_2)_{16}COOH$. Its name comes from the Greek word stear, which means tallow. Its IUPAC name is octadecanoic acid.[123]

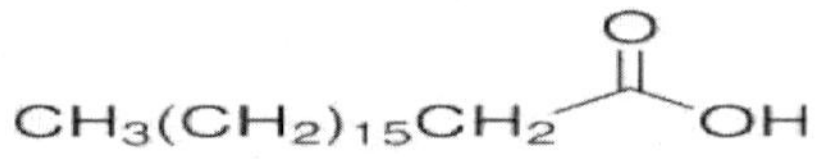

$$CH_3(CH_2)_{15}CH_2 \overset{\overset{\displaystyle O}{\parallel}}{C} OH$$

Fig. 5.3: Structure of Stearic acid

Chemical Names:

Stearic acid; Octadecanoic acid; 57-11-4; Stearophanic acid; N-Octadecanoic acid.

Molecular   Formula:

$CH_3(CH_2)_{16}COOH$ / $C_{18}H_{36}O_2$ or $CH_3(CH_2)_{16}COOH$ or C18H36O2.

Molecular Weight: 284.484 g/mol.

Uses

In general, the applications of stearic acid exploit its bifunctional character, with a polar head group that can be attached to metal cations and a nonpolar chain that confers solubility in organic solvents. The combination leads to uses as a surfactant and softening agent. Stearic acid undergoes the typical reactions of saturated carboxylic acids, a notable one being reduction to stearyl alcohol, and esterification with a range of alcohols. This is used in a large range of manufactures, from simple to complex electronic devices.

5.2.3 Tween 80

Polysorbate 80 is a nonionic surfactant and emulsifier often used in foods and cosmetics. This synthetic compound is a viscous, water-soluble yellow liquid. [124]

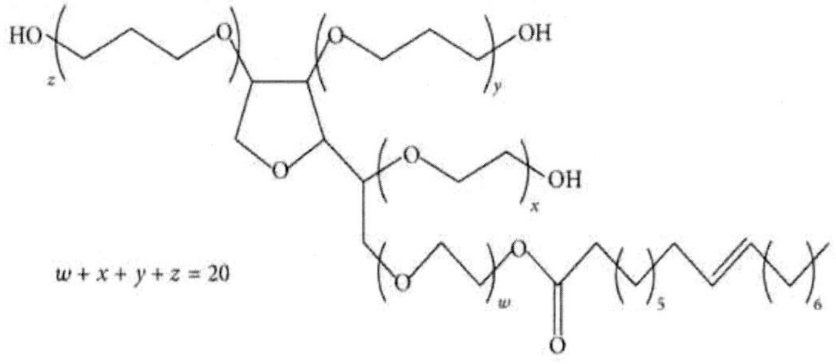

$w + x + y + z = 20$

Fig. 5.4: Structure of Tween 80

Chemical Names:

Tween 80; AC1L9EF8; 2-[2-[3,4-bis(2-hydroxyethoxy)oxolan-2-yl]-2-(2-hydroxyethoxy)ethoxy]ethyl octadec-9-enoate.

Molecular Formula: $C_{32}H_{60}O_{10}$

Molecular Weight: 604.822 g/mol

Uses

Polysorbate 80 is an excipient that is used to stabilize aqueous formulations of medications for parenteral administration, and used as an emulsifier in the manufacture of the popular antiarrhythmic amiodarone. It is also used as an excipient in some European and Canadian influenza vaccines. Influenza vaccines contain 25 µg of polysorbate 80 per dose. It is also used in the culture of *Mycobacterium tuberculosis* in Middlebrook 7H9 broth. It is also used as an emulsifier in the estrogen-regulating drug .

PREFORMULATION STUDIES

6.1 Preformulation

6.2 Characterization of drug:

6.2.1 Physiochemical Properties of Oxaprozin

A) Physical evaluation

It refers to the evaluation by sensory characters appearance, odor, feel of the drug, etc [125].

Table 6.1: List of Sensory characters

S. No.	Sensory characters	Result
1.	Colour	White to off-white powder
2.	Odour	Slight odour

B) Solubility: Solubility of the drug was determined by taking some quantity of drug (about 1-2 mg) in the test tube separately and added the 5 ml of the solvent (Water, ethanol, methanol, 0.1N HCl, 0.1N NaOH, and 7.4 pH buffer) Shake vigorously and kept for some time. Note the solubility of the drug in various solvents (at room temperature) [126].

Table 6.2: Solubility of Oxaprozin [127]

Solvent used	Solubility	Results
Distilled Water	Insoluble	- - -
0.1 N Hydrochloric acid	Slightly Soluble	+
Ethanol	Soluble	+++
Methanol	Slightly Soluble	+
0.1 N NaOH	Sparingly soluble	++
Phosphate buffer pH 7.4	Sparingly soluble	++

Freely soluble	1-10 Parts	++++
Soluble	10-30 Parts	+++
Sparingly soluble	30-100 Parts	++
Slightly soluble	100-1000 Parts	+
Practically insoluble	greater than 1000	- - -

C) Melting point:

It is one of the parameters to judge the purity of drugs. In case of pure chemicals, melting points are very sharp and constant. Since the drugs contain the mixed chemicals, they are described with certain range of melting point [128].

Procedure for determine melting point:

A small quantity of powder was placed into a fusion tube. That tube was placed in the melting point determining apparatus (Chemline CL-725) containing castor oil. The temperature of the castor oil was gradual increased automatically and read the temperature at which powder started to melt and the temperature when all the powder gets melted.

Table 6.3: Melting point of Oxaprozin

S. No.	Standard Melting Point of Oxaprozin	Practical Melting Point of Oxaprozin
1.	158-159 °C	162°C to 163°C

D) Identification Test

FTIR Spectroscopy

Infra- red spectrum is an important record which gives sufficient information about the structure of a compound. This technique provides a spectrum containing a large number of absorption band from which a wealth of information can be derived about the structure of an organic compound. The region from 0.8 μ to 2.5 μ is called Near Infra-red and that from 15 μ to 200 μ is called Far infra-red region

Identification of Oxaprozin was done by FTIR Spectroscopy with respect to marker compound. Oxaprozin was obtained as White to off-white powder. It was identified from the result of IR spectrum as per specification.

Sample of pure Oxaprozin

The IR spectrum of sample drug shows the peak values which are characteristics of the drug and the graph were shown in fig no. 6.2

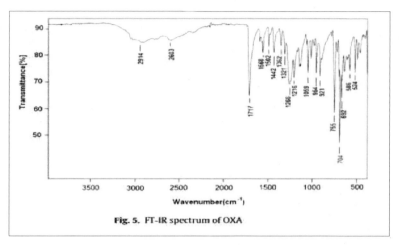

Fig. 5. FT-IR spectrum of OXA

Fig. 6.1: FT-IR Spectrum of Pure Drug (Oxaprozin standard) [129]

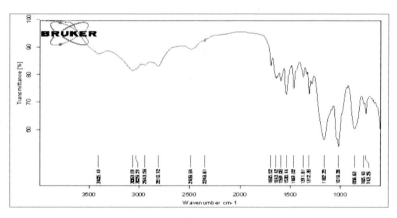

Fig. 6.2: FT-IR Spectrum of Pure Drug (Oxaprozin sample)

Table 6.4: IR Interpretation of Oxaprozin

S. No.	Group	Peak Position
1	OH $_{str.}$	2913.93
2	C=O$_{str.}$	1825.52
3	OH	1461.82
4	C-GYYUGYU	1262.23
5	O-H$_{Bend}$	896.93

E) Loss on drying: The moisture in a solid can be expressed on a wet weight or dry wet basis. On a wet weight basis, the water content of a material is calculated as a percentage of the weight of the weight solid. The term loss on drying is an expression of moisture content on a wet weight basis.

Procedure:

Loss on drying is directly measured by Hot air oven. Take 1gm sample (powder) and set the temp at 100°C to 105°C for 15 minutes and constant reading set the knob and check % moisture.

$$\% LOD = \frac{Initial\,weight - Final\,weight}{Initial\,weight} X100$$

Table 6.5: Loss of drying of drug sample

S. No.	Initial weight	Final weight after 15 minutes	% loss of drying
1.	1gm	0.989 gm	1.1 %

F) Moisture content determination:

Principle: The titrimetric determination of water is based upon the quantitative reaction of water with an anhydrous solution of sulphur dioxide and iodine in the presence of a buffer that reacts with hydrogen ions.

Procedure

Karl Fischer coulometry is a micro-method and is particularly suitable for samples with low water content, from 10 µg up to 10 mg. Here, the required iodine is generated electrochemically in the titration vessel by anodic oxidation from iodide contained in the coulometric reagents. The amount of consumed electric charge is used to calculate the consumption of iodine and therefore the amount of water in the sample.

Formula:- Moisture Content in mg = KF Factor X KF Reagent consumed

Table 6.6: Moisture content determination

S. No.	Drug	KF Factor	Amount of KF	Moisture

			Reagent consumed (ml)	content (mg)
1	Oxaprozin	0.362	0.21ml	0.0760

Moisture content in drug or formulation plays an important role to check the accurate purity of pure drug.

G) Determination of λ max of Oxaprozin:

The λ_{max} of Oxaprozin was determined by running the spectrum of drug solution in double beam ultraviolet spectrophotometer [130].

Procedure:

Accurately weighed 10 mg of drug was dissolved in 10 ml of 7.4 pH buffer solution in 10 ml of volumetric flask. The resulted solution 1000μg/ml and from this solution 1 ml pipette out and transfer into 10 ml volumetric flask and volume make up with 7.4 pH buffer solution prepare suitable dilution to make it to a concentration range of 5-25μg/ml. The spectrum of this solution was run in 200-400 nm range in U.V. spectrophotometer (Labindia-3000+). The spectrum peak point graph of absorbance of Oxaprozin versus wave length was shown in fig. 6.3

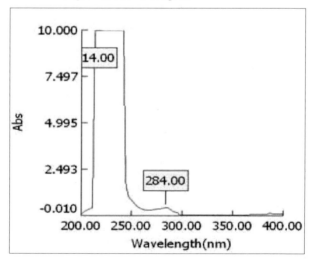

Fig. 6.3: Wavelength maxima of Oxaprozin in 7.4 pH buffer solution

44

H) Calibration curve of Oxaprozin at λ $_{max}$ 284nm

Observation table:

Table 6.7: Calibration curve of Oxaprozin

S. No.	Conc. (µg/ml)	Absorbance
1	5	0.135
2	10	0.258
3	15	0.387
4	20	0.509
5	25	0.611

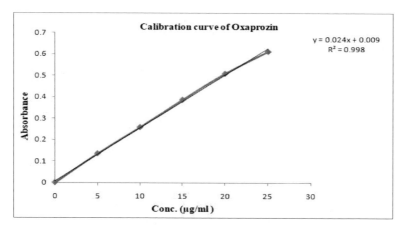

Fig. 6.4: Calibration curve of Oxaprozin in pH 7.4 at 284nm

The linear regression analysis was done on Absorbance data points. The results are as follow for standard curve

Slope	=	0.024
The intercept	=	0.009
The correlation coefficient (r^2)	=	0.998

FORMULATION AND CHARACTERIZATION

Solid lipid nanoparticles (SLN) are aqueous colloid-al dispersions, the matrix of which comprises of solid biodegradable lipids. SLNs combine the advantages and avoid the

45

drawbacks of several colloidal carriers of its class such as physical stability, protection of incorporated labile drugs from degradation, controlled release, and excellent tolerability. [131]

Method of preparation of SLN

- High shear homogenization (HSH)
- Ultrasonication
- Microemulsion based SLN preparation
- Supercritical Fluid technology Solvent emulsification/evaporation
- Solvent emulsification-diffusion
- Double Emulsion
- Spray Drying
- Solvent injection technique

On the basis of fiesability and availativity of chemicals, and following advantages the Solvent injection technique used for preparation of SLN [132]

- Good tolerability,
- Lower cytotoxicity,
- Higher bioavailability by oral administration,
- Possibility of controlled release,
- Increase in the drug stability
- Cost effectiveness

7.1.1 Formulation of Oxaprozin loaded solid lipid nanoparticles

Procedure

Method: solvent injection technique using ethanol as organic solvent

Step I: Soya lecithin, drug and steric acid is dissolved in the ethanol in definite ratio and warmed to 70°C.

Step II: The phosphate buffer solution (pH 7.4) a definite amount of tween 80 is added to prepare aqueous phase and kept for stirring which is maintain at 70°C.

Step III: The organic phase was added drop wise with stirring to the pre warmed aqueous solution with the help of hypodermic needle. The mixture was then sonicated (Ultra sonicator, Bath type, Electronic India) for varying time to obtain nanoparticles.

Table7.1: Formulation development of SLN

Components	Formulation code					
	F1	F2	F3	F4	F5	F6
Drug (mg)	100	100	100	100	100	100
Soya lecithin (mg)	25	50	75	100	125	150
Steric acid(mg)	75	75	75	75	75	75
Tween 80(ml)	0.5	0.5	0.5	0.5	0.5	0.5
Sonication time (min)	5	5	5	5	5	5

In the SLN Formulations (F1 to F6), the Soya lecithin ratio was optimized by taking their different ratio such as 25, 50, 75, 100, 125 and 150mg and all other parameters were kept remain constant. The prepared formulations were optimized on the basis of average particle size and % entrapment efficiency.

7.2 Evaluation of solid lipid nanoparticles [133]

7.2.1 Particle size and zeta potential

The vesicles size and size distribution and surface charge were determined by Dynamic Light Scattering method (DLS) (Malvern Zetamaster, ZEM 5002, Malvern, UK, SOPS RGPV, Bhopal (M.P.). Zeta potential measurement of the elastic liposomes was based on the zeta potential that was calculated according to Helmholtz – Smoluchowsky from their electrophoretic mobility[134].For measurement of zeta potential, a zetasizer was used with field strength of 20 V/cm on a large bore measures cell. Samples were diluted with 0.9 % NaCl adjusted to a conductivity of 50 lS/cm.

7.2.2 Entrapment efficiency

0.1mL of freshly prepared formulation was taken and diluted with 9.9 mL with phosphate buffer of pH 7.4. The obtained suspension was vortexed for 1 h and centrifuged for 45min at 6,000rpm. The supernatant was separated and filtered through 0.2μm filter. The filtrate was diluted using phosphate buffer of pH 7.4 and analysed at 284nm using UV spectrophotometer (Labindia 3000 plus). The SLNs formulated without drug were treated similarly and used as control for the measurements[135]. The assay was repeated 3 times using different preparations. Entrapment efficiency was calculated as shown below:

$$\% \text{ Entrapment Efficiency} = \frac{Th\,hhh\,erotical\,drug\,content - Practical\,drug\,content}{Therotical\,drug\,content} \times 100$$

Table7.2: Result for Entrapment efficiency of drug loaded SLN

Formulation Code	Entrapment Efficiency*
F1	65.56±0.25
F2	68.98±0.36
F3	75.65±0.32
F4	62.23±0.45
F5	58.98±0.58
F6	52.12±0.65

*Average of three Determinations

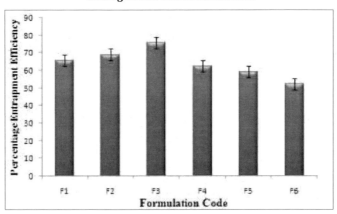

Table7.3: Particle size and Entrapment efficiency of Optimized SLN

Formulation Code	Particle size (nm)	% Entrapment Efficiency	Zeta potential (mV)
F3	402.1	75.65±0.32	-20.2

Table7.4: Zeta Potential value and Interpretation

Zeta Potential (mV)	Stability Behavior
0 to ± 5	Rapid coagulation / flocculation
± 10 to ±30	Incipient instability
±30 to ±40	Moderate stability
±40 to ±60	Good stability

MT ±60	Excellent stability

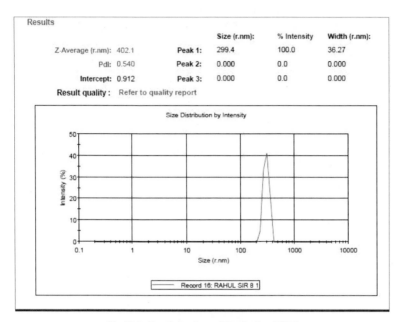

Fig. 7.1: Particle size of Optimized SLN

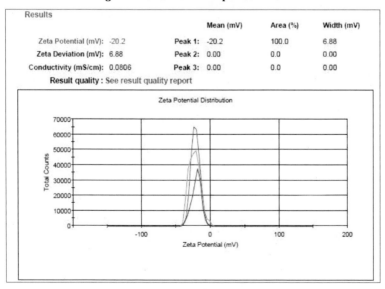

Fig. 7.2: Zeta potential of Optimized SLN

7.2.4 *In vitro* drug release study

The cellophane membrane approximately 25cm × 2cm was taken and washed in the running water. It was then soaked in distilled water for 24 hours, before used for diffusion studies to remove glycerin present on it and was mounted on the diffusion cell for further studies.

Oxaprozin-SLNs formulation was injected into a dialysis bag and dialyzed against 18 mL PBS (pH 7.4) containing 0.3% tween 80 (v/v) (receiver solution) in a 25 mL tube at 24 °C and 37 °C with shaking at 130 rpm. Plain oxaprozin (with the same amount of drug as the formulation) was also filled with a dialysis bag with the same pore size and dialyzed against 18 mL 0.3% (v/v) tween 80 to examine the permeability of the membrane to the drug. At fixed time points, 2 mL of samples were gathered from the receiver solution and the same amount of fresh medium was added back to the medium. The oxaprozin in the collected samples were assayed spectrophotometrically at wavelength 284 nm. [136].

The observations of drug release from the SLN formulation is tabulated in Table 7.5.

Table7.5: Cumulative % drug release of Oxaprozin loaded SLN

S. No.	Time (hrs)	% Cumulative Drug Release*
1	0.5	19.89±0.56
2	1	25.65±0.32
3	2	35.65±0.45
4	4	48.98±0.52
5	6	55.65±0.14
6	8	68.89±0.23
7	10	75.65±0.32
8	12	78.98±0.98

*Average of three Determinations

7.2.5 Release kinetics

In-vitro dissolution has been recognized as an important element in drug development. Under certain conditions it can be used as a surrogate for the assessment of bioequivalence. Several theories/kinetic models describe drug dissolution from immediate and modified release dosage forms. There are several models to represent the drug dissolution profiles where ft is the function of t (time) related to the amount of drug dissolved from the pharmaceutical dosage system. To compare dissolution profiles between two drug products model dependent (curve fitting), statistic analysis and model independent methods can be used.

In order to elucidate mode and mechanism of drug release, the *In vitro* data was transformed and interpreted at graphical interface constructed using various kinetic models. The zero order release Eq. (1) describes the drug dissolution of several types of modified release pharmaceutical dosage forms, as in the case of transdermal systems, matrix tablets with low soluble drugs, coated forms, osmotic systems etc., where the drug release is independent of concentration.

$Qt = Qo + Kot$ (1)

Where, Qt is the amount of drug released in time t, Qo is the initial amount of the drug in the solution and Ko is the zero order release constant

The first order Eq. (2) describes the release from the system where release is concentration dependent e.g. pharmaceutical dosage forms containing water soluble drugs in porous matrices.

$logQt = log\ Qo + K1\ t\ /2.303$ (2)

Where Qt is the amount of drug released in time t, Q is the initial amount of drug in the solution and K1 is the first order release constant.

Higuchi described the release of drug from insoluble matrix as a square root of time as given in Eq. (3)

$Qt = KH\ \sqrt{t}$ (3)

Where, Qt is the amount of drug released in time t, KH is Higuchi's dissolution constant. The following plots were made: cumulative % drug release vs. time (zero order kinetic models); log cumulative of % drug remaining vs. time (first order kinetic model); log cumulative % drug release vs. log time (Korsmeyer - peppas model).

Table7.6: *In Vitro* Drug Release Data for F3

S. No.	Time (H)	Square Root of Time	Log Time	Cumulative * Percentage Drug Release±SD	Log Cumulative Percentage Drug Release	Cumulative Percent Drug Remaining	Log cumulative Percent Drug Remaining

1	0.5	0.707	-0.301	19.89	1.298	80.11	1.903
2	1	1.000	0.000	25.65	1.409	74.35	1.871
3	2	1.414	0.301	35.65	1.552	64.35	1.808
4	4	2.000	0.602	48.98	1.690	51.02	1.707
5	6	2.449	0.778	55.65	1.745	44.35	1.646
6	8	2.828	0.903	68.89	1.838	31.11	1.492
7	10	3.162	1.000	75.65	1.878	24.35	1.386
8	12	3.464	1.079	78.98	1.897	21.02	1.322

* Average of three determinations

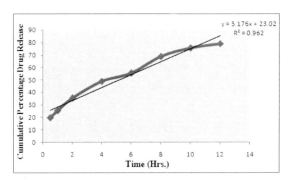

Figure 7.3:Cumulative Percent Drug Released Vs Time (Zero Order Plots)

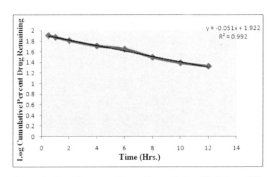

Figure 7.4: Log Cumulative Percent Drug Remaining Vs Time (First Order Plots)

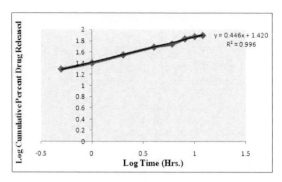

Figure 7.5: Log Cumulative Percent Drug Released Vs Log Time (Peppas Plots)

Table7.7: Regression Analysis Data of SLN Formulation

Formulation	Zero order	First order	Pappas plot
F3	$R^2 = 0.962$	$R^2 = 0.992$	$R^2 = 0.996$

7.2.6 Stability studies

Table7.8: Effect of Storage on Particle Size and Percent Entrapment Efficiency of SLN

Parameters	Initial Observation	After 30 days	
		At 4ºC	At 25± 2°C ºC
Particle Size (µm)	402.1±0.45	398.2±0.25	565.56±1.25
Percent Entrapment Efficiency	75.65±0.32	72.12±0.45	65.56±1.32

Stability studies were carried out with optimized formulation which was stored for a period of 30 days at 4±1°C and 25± 2°C ºC. The particle size of formulation was determined by particle size analyzer. The particle size of the SLN was found to increase at RT, which may be attributed to the aggregation of SLN at higher temperature. At 25± 2°C °C the SLN aggregate i.e. these SLN were unstable at higher temperature like 25±2°C. Percent efficiency of SLN also decreases at higher temperature like 25± 2°C °C.

The overall objective of preformulation testing is to generate information useful to the formulator in developing stable and bioavailable dosage forms which can be mass-produced. Preformulation studies are essential protocols for improvement of safety, efficacy and stability of dosage form as well. Thus it plays an important role in order to ensure optimum condition for clinically advantageous delivery system.

Color of the Oxaprozin was found to be white to off-white crystalline powder and slight odor and taste. One important goal of the pre-formulation studies is to devise a method to check the Solubility of drug. Solubility of the drug was determined by taking weighed quantity of drug (about 1-2 mg) in the test tube separately and added the 10 ml of the solvent. Oxaprozin was practically insoluble in water, slightly soluble in 0.1 N HCl, soluble in ethanol, slightly soluble in methanol. Sparingly soluble in 0.1 N NaOH, Sparingly soluble in phosphate buffer pH 7.4. Melting point was determined by Melting point apparatus using open capillary method and found to be in the range of 162°C to 163°C for Oxaprozin. FTIR spectroscopy: Identification of Oxaprozin sample was done by infrared spectroscopy. Loss on drying is directly measured by IR moisture balance. Firstly 1.00 gm of drug (powder) was taken and temp was set at 100°C to 105°C for 15 minutes and constant reading was taken again set the knob and check % moisture. The percentage of loss on drying of Oxaprozin was found to be 1.1 % w/w respectively.

Moisture content determination was done by Karl Fischer colorimetric method. Moisture content of Oxaprozin was found 0.0760mg. Identification of Oxaprozin was performed by UV/VIS Spectroscopy. The 10µg/ml solutions of Oxaprozin was scanned in the range of 200-400nm to determine the wavelength of maximum absorption for drug. The λ_{max} of Oxaprozin was found to be 284nm. From the respective stock solution (1mg/ml) different concentration of 5-25 µg/ml Oxaprozin was prepared and scanned in UV region. Their absorbances were noted at Λmax, 284 nm and calibration curve was plotted as absorbance vs concentration and their linearity range was determined.

Solid Lipid Nanoparticles (SLNs) are important because of their size and stability. SLNs have been reported as an alternative drug delivery device to traditional polymeric nanoparticles. SLNs are in submicron range (50-1000nm) and are composed of physiologically tolerated lipid components. At room temperature the particles are in solid state. They are made up of bio-compatible and bio-degradable materials capable of incorporating lipophilic and hydrophilic drugs.

Oxaprozin loaded solid lipid nano-particles were prepared by solvent injection method. Optimization of process and formulation parameters resulted in the production of Oxaprozin loaded SLNs with particle size 402.1nm and entrapment efficiency of 75.65±0.32% of Optimized SLN formulation F3.

In-vitro release studies were performed in PBS (pH 7.4) for 12 hrs. From the cumulative % drug release data, it was observed that about 78.98% of the drug were released from optimized formulation F3 of Oxaprozin loaded SLNs. It was found that the *in-vitro* drug release of the Oxaprozin loaded SLNs was best explained by Pappas release Kinetics as the plot showed highest linearity (R^2= 0.996). Zero order (R^2=0.962), First order (R^2=0.992), Pappas plot (R^2=0.996) of regression analysis data of SLN F3 Formulation.

Oxaprozin is a non-narcotic, non-steroidal anti-inflammatory drug (NSAID), used to relieve the inflammation, swelling, stiffness, and joint pain associated with osteoarthritis and rheumatoid arthritis.

Solid lipid nanoparticles (SLN) introduced in 1991 represent an alternative carrier system to tradition colloidal carriers such as emulsions, liposomes and polymeric micro and nanoparticles. Nanoparticles made from solid lipids are attracting major attention as novel colloidal drug carrier for intravenous applications as they have been proposed as an alternative particulate carrier system. SLN are sub-micron colloidal carriers ranging from 50 to 1000 nm, which are composed of physiological lipid, dispersed in water or in aqueous surfactant solution. SLN offer unique properties such as small size, large surface area, high drug loading and the interaction of phases at the interface and are attractive for their potential to improve performance of pharmaceuticals. The Solid lipid nanoparticles were successfully developed for systemic delivery of Oxaprozin. SLN dispersions were prepared by solvent injection method. Physicochemical characterization including particle size, particle size distribution, Zeta potential, scanning electron microscopy and *in-vitro* release profile were carried out. *In-vitro* drug release pattern of optimized formulation of SLN showed fast and control release.

References

1. Panchagnula R. Transdermal delivery of drugs. Indian J Pharmacol. 1997; 29:140–56.
2. Rao PR, Diwan PV. Formulation and *in vitro* evaluation of polymeric films of diltiazem hydrochloride and indomethacin for transdermal administration. Drug Dev Indian Pharm. 1998; 24:327–36.
3. Rao PR, Diwan PV. Permeability studies of cellulose acetate free films for transdermal use: Influence of plasticizers. Pharm Acta Helv. 1997; 72:47–51.
4. Thacharodi D, Rap KP. Development and *in vitro* evaluation of chitosan-based trandermal drug delivery system for the controlled delivery of propranolol hydrochloride. Biomaterials. 1995; 16:145–8.
5. Krishna R, Pandit JK. Carboxymethylcellulose-sodium based transdermal drug delivery system for propranolol. J Pharm Pharmacol. 1996; 48:367–70.
6. Bhat M, Shenoy DS, Udupa N, Srinivas CR. Optimization of delivery of betamethasone - dipropionate from skin preparation. Indian Drugs. 1995; 32:211–4.
7. Joseph Robinson and Vincent H. L. Lee, Controlled Drug Delivery - Fundamentals and Applications, 2nd Edition, 4-33.
8. GatesKAetal.PharmRes1994; 11:1605,1609.
9. BanakerUV.AmPharm1987; 2:39,48.
10. Muller RH, Runge SA. Solid lipid nanoparticles (SLN) for controlled drug delivery. In: Benita S, editor. Submicron emulsions in drug targeting and delivery. Harwood Academic Pub, 22(7), 1998, 219-234.
11. Reddy. P.D., Swarnalatha D. Recent advances in Novel Drug Delivery Systems. IJPTR, 2010; 2(3): 2025-2027.
12. Manivannan R. Recent Advances in Novel Drug Delivery System. IJRAP. 2010; 1(2); 316-326.
13. Siavash Iravani, Behzad Zolfaghari. Green synthesis of silver nanoparticles using Pinus eldarica bark extract. Hindawi Publishing Corporation, Biomed. Res. Int. 2013; 5: 1-5.
14. Naheed Ahmad, Seema Sharma. Green synthesis of silver nanoparticles using extracts of Ananas comosus. Green Sustainable Chem. 2012; 2: 141-147.

15. C. Shah, V. Shah, U. Upadhyay, solid lipid nanoparticles: a review current pharma research, 2011; 1(4):351-368.

16. Rajasekhar Chokkareddy and Gan G. Redhi, Green Synthesis of Metal Nanoparticles and its Reaction Mechanisms: Synthesis, Characterization and Their Applications,2018, 113-139

17. Ladj, R., Bitar, A., Eissa, M., Mugnier, Y., Le Dantec, R., Fessi, H., Elaissari, A. Individual inorganic nanoparticles: preparation, functionalization and in vitro biomedical diagnostic applications. J. Mater. Chem. B, 2013; 1: 1381-1396.

18. Mark Asta, Susan M. Kauzlarich, Kai Liu, Alexandra Navrotsky, Frank, E. Osterlohinorganic nanoparticles unique properties and novel applications. Mater. Matters.2007; 2(1):12-19.

19. Mukherjee S, Ray S, Thakur RS. Solid lipid nanoparticles: a modern formulation approach in drug delivery system. Indian J Pharm Sci. 2009; 71(4):349-58.

20. Houli Li, Xiaobin Zhao, Yukun Ma and Guangxi Zhai, Ling Bing Li and Hong Xiang, Lou. J. Cont.Release, 133, 238-244 (2009).

21. Houli Li, Xiaobin Zhao, Yukun Ma and Guangxi Zhai, Ling Bing Li and Hong Xiang, Lou. Enhancement of gastrointestinal absorption of quercetin by solid lipid nanoparticles, journal of controlled release. J. Cont. Release.2009; 133: 238-244.

22. Melike Uner, Gulgun Yener. Importance of solid lipid nanoparticles (SLN) in various administration routes and future perspectives. Int. J. Nanomedicine. 2007; 2(3): 289-300.

23. Indu Pal Kaur, Rohit Bhandari, Swati Bhandari and Kakkur. Potential of solid lipid nanoparticles in brain targeting. J. Cont. Rel. 2008; 127: 97-109.

24. S. Mukherjee, S. Ray and R. S. Thakur, Ind. J. Pharm. Sci.,2009,349-358

25. Rainer H. Muller, Karsten Mader and Sven Gohla, Eur. J. Pharm. Biopharm., 50(1),2000, 161-177

26. Wolfgang Mehnart and Karsten Mader, Adv. Drug. Deliv. Rev., 47,2001,165-196

27. Wolfgang Mehnart and Karsten Mader. Solid lipid nanoparticles: production, characterization and applications. Adv. Drug. Deliv. Rev. 2001; 47:165-196.

28. Garud, A., Singh,D.and Garud, N.(2012). Solid Lipid Nanoparticles (SLN): Method, Characterization andApplication. International Current Pharmaceutical Journal., 1(11),384-393.

29. K. Sharma, A. Diwan, S. Sardana, V. Dhall. Int. J. Research in Pharma., 2011; 2(3):450-461

30. Mehnart and K. Mader. Problem associated with SLN. Adv. drug delivery review. 2011; 47:165-195

31. M Uner; G Yener. Int J Nanomedicine., 2007, 2(3), 289–300.

32. Jannin, J. Musakhanian, D. Marchaud. Approaches for the development of solid and semi-solid lipid-based formulations. Adv. Drug Del.Reviews,2008; 60:734–746.

33. Abdelbary and R. H. Fahmy. Amer. Asso. Of Pharma. Techno., 2009; 10(1).

34. Yadav, G. Soni, A. Mahor, P. P. Singh and A. Varma. Int. J. Pharma. Sci. and Research, 2014; 5(3):1152-1162.

35. Verma, S. and Makkar, D. (2016). Solid Lipid nanoparticles: a comprehensive review. Journal ofChemical and Pharmaceutical Research., 8(8),102-114.

36. S Jaiswal; GD Gupta. IAJPR., 2013, 3(12), 1601-1611

37. Antonio J. Almeida and Eliana Souto. Solid lipid nanoparticles as a drug delivery system for peptides and proteins. Adv. Drug Delivery Rev. 2007; 59: 478-490.

38. Mishra, B. B. Patel, S. Tiwar. Colloidal Nano carrierNano medicine, 2010; 6(1):9-24.

39. S. P. Vyas and R. K. Khar, Controlled Drug Delivery - Concepts and Advances, First Edition, Vallabh Prakashan. 2002; 38-50.

40. J Patil, P Gurav, R Kulkarni, S Jadhav, S Mandave, M Shete, V Chipade. Applications of solid lipid nanoparticle in novel drug delivery system. Br. biomed bull. 2013; 1(2):103-118.

41. CT Tzache, HL Svilenov. Int. J. Pharm. Sci. Rev. Res. 2013; 18(1): 103-115.

42. Ekambaram, A. H. Sathali, K. Priyanka, et al. Solid Lipid Nanoparticles: Scientific Review and Chemical Communication, 2012; 2(1):80-102

43. Manjunath, V. Venkateswarlu. Preparation, Characterization and In Vitro Rel. Kinetics of Clozapine Solid Lipid Nanoparticles. J. cont.Rel.., 2012; 95: 627-638.

44. B Magenheim, MY Levy, S Benita. A new in vitro technique for the evaluation of drug release profile from colloidal carriers - ultrafiltration technique at low pressure. Int. J. Pharm. 1993; 94: 115–123.

45. Q. Hu, H. Yuan, H. H. Zhang, M. Fang, et al. Preparation of solid lipid nanoparticles with clobetasol propionate by a novel solvent diffusion method in

aqueous system and physicochemical characterization. Int.J. Pharma., 2012; 239:121–128

46. Lv , A. Yu , H. Li , Z. Song et al. Development and evaluation of penciclovir-loaded solid lipid nanoparticles for topical delivery. Int.J.Pharm., 2009; 372:191–198

47. Charcosset , A. El-Harati , H. Fessi et al. Preparation of solid lipid nanoparticles using a membrane contactor. J. Controlled Rel., 2005; 108 :112–12

48. Yadav, S. Khatak, S.U. Vir Singhet al. Int.J. Applied Pharm. 2013; 5(2):8-18.

49. SM Pallerla, B Prabhakar. A Review on Solid Lipid Nanoparticles. Int. J. Pharm. Sci. Rev. Res. 2013; 20(2): 196-206.

50. Qing Zhi Lu, Aihua Yu, Yanwei Xi and Houli Li, Zhimei Song, Jing Cui and Fengliang Cao, Guangxi Zhai, Int. J. Pharm., 372, 191 – 198 (2009).

51. Rishi Paliwal, Shivani Rai, Bhuvaneshwar Vaidya, Kapil Khatri, Amit K. Goyal, Neeraj Mishra, Abhinav Mehta and Suresh P. Vyas, PhD. Nanomedicine, Nanotechnology, Biology and Medicine, 5(2), (2009) pp. 184-191.

52. Annette Zur Mehlen, Cora Schwarz and Wolfgang Mehnart, Eur. J. Pharm. Biopharm., 45,1998,149-155

53. P. Vyas and R. K. Khar, Controlled Drug Delivery - Concepts and Advances, First Edition, Vallabh Prakashan .2002,38-50.

54. Praveen Kumar Gupta, J. K. Pandit, Ajay Kumar and Pallavi Swaroop, Sanjiv gupta, T. Ph. Res., 3, 117-138 (2010).

55. M Uner; G Yener. Int J Nanomedicine., 2007, 2(3), 289–300.

56. Qing Zhi Lu, Aihua Yu, Yanwei Xi and Houli Li, Zhimei Song, Jing Cui and Fengliang Cao, Guangxi Zhai. Development and evaluation of penciclovir-loaded solid lipid nanoparticles for topical delivery. Int. J. Pharm. 2009; 372: 191-198.

57. Yi Fan Luo, Da Wei Chen, Li Xiang Ren and Xiu Li Zhao, Jing Qin. Solid lipid nanoparticles for enhancing vinpocetine's oral bioavailability. J. Cont. Release. 2006; 114: 53–59.

58. Rishi Paliwal, Shivani Rai, Bhuvaneshwar Vaidya, Kapil Khatri, Amit K. Goyal, Neeraj Mishra, Abhinav Mehta and Suresh P. Vyas, Nanomedicine, Nanotechnology, Biology and Medicine. 2009; 5(2): 184-191.

59. Ghada Abdelbary and Rania H. Fahmy. Diazepam-Loaded Solid Lipid Nanoparticles: Design and Characterization. AAPS Pharm. Sci. Tech. 2009; 10(1): 211–219.

60. Alessandro Bargoni, Roberto Cavalla, Otto Caputo and M. R Gasco. A review on solid lipid nanoparticles. Pharm. Res. 1998; 15(5):745-750.

61. Milan Stuchlik and Stanislav Zak. Biomed, Papers. Lipid-based vehicle for oral drug delivery. 2001; 145(2): 17-26.

62. C. Olbrich and R. H. Muller. Enzymatic degradation of SLN-effect of surfactant and surfactant mixtures. Int. J. Pharm.1999; 180: 31-39.

63. D. Schwarz, W. Mehnert, J. S. Lucks and R. H. Muller. Solid lipid nanoparticles (SLN) for controlled drug delivery. I. Production, characterization and sterilization. J. Cont. Release. 1994; 30(1): 83-96.

64. Wei Liu, Meling Hu, Wehsuang Liu and Chengbin Xue, Huibi Xu. Investigation of the carbopol gel of solid lipid nanoparticles for the transdermal iontophoretic delivery of triamcinolone acetonide acetate. Int. J. Pharm.2008; 364: 141-146.

65. Qing Zhi Lu, Aihua Yu, Yanwei Xi and Houli Li, Zhimei Song, Jing Cui and Fengliang Cao, Guangxi Zhai. Development and evaluation of Penciclovir – loaded Solid lipid nanoparticles for topical delivery. Int. J. Pharm. 2009; 372: 191-198.

66. A Tiwari; S Rashi; S Anand. Solid lipid nanoparticles as carriers in drug delivery system. World journal of pharmacy and pharmaceutical sciences. 2015; 4(8): 337-355.

67. I Sarathchandiran. A review on nanotechnology in solid lipid nanoparticles. International Journal of Pharmaceutical Development & Technology. 2012; 2(1): 45-61.

68. L Battaglia, M Gallarate, PP Panciani, E Ugazio, S Sapino, E Peira, D Chirio. Intech. 2014; 49-75.

69. Sven Gohla, Eur. J. Pharm. Biopharm., 50,2007 ,161-177

70. Amaldoss ,M J Newton , SukhjinderKaur Solid lipid nanoparticles for skin and drug delivery: Methods of preparation and characterization techniques and applications Nanoarchitectonics in Biomedicine 2019, 295-334

71. Fakhar ud Din ,Alam Zeb ,Kifayat Ullah Shaha ,Zia-ur-Rehman. Development, in-vitro and in-vivo evaluation of ezetimibe-loaded solid lipid nanoparticles and their comparison with marketed product. Journal of Drug Delivery Science and Technology ,51,2019,583-590

72. Aldemar Gordillo - Galeano, Claudia Elizabeth, Mora-Huertas. Solid lipid nanoparticles and nanostructured lipid carriers: A review emphasizing on particle structure and drug release. European Journal of Pharmaceutics and Biopharmaceutics.133, 2018, 285-308

73. Huaixiang Tian,Zhuoyan Lu,Danfeng Li,JingHu. Preparation and characterization of citral-loaded solid lipid nanoparticles.Food Chemistry.248, 2018, 78-85

74. Christos Tapeinos, Matteo Battaglini, Gianni Ciofani. Advances in the design of solid lipid nanoparticles and nanostructured lipid carriers for targeting brain diseases. Journal of Controlled Release. 2017; 306-332.

75. Chih-Hung Lin, Chun-Han Chen, Zih-Chan Lin, Jia-You Fang. Recent advances in oral delivery of drugs and bioactive natural products using solid lipid nanoparticles as the carriers. Journal of food and drug analysis. 2017; 8: 1-16.

76. Leila Azhar Shekoufeh Bahari, Hamed Hamishehkar. The Impact of Variables on Particle Size of Solid Lipid Nanoparticles and Nanostructured Lipid Carriers; A Comparative Literature Review. Advanced Pharmaceutical Bulletin. 2016; 6(2): 143-151.

77. Malgorzata Geszke-Moritz, Michal Moritz. Solid lipid nanoparticles as attractive drug vehicles: Composition, properties and therapeutic strategies. Materials Science & Engineering C. 2016; 68:982-994.

78. Neda Naseri, Hadi Valizadeh, Parvin Zakeri-Milani. Solid Lipid Nanoparticles and Nanostructured Lipid Carriers: Structure, Preparation and Application. Advanced Pharmaceutical Bulletin. 2015; 5(3):305-313.

79. Yangchao Luo,Zi Teng,Ying Li, QinWang. Solid lipid nanoparticles for oral drug delivery: Chitosan coating improves stability, controlled delivery, mucoadhesion and cellular uptake. Carbohydrate Polymers.122, 2015, 221-229

80. Yadav V, AlokMahor S, Alok S, AmitaVerma A, Kumar N, Kumar S. Solid lipid nanoparticles (sln): formulation by high pressure homogenization. World J Pharm Pharm Sci. 2014;3(11):1200–13

81. KinamPark. Controlled drug delivery systems: Past forward and future back. Journal of Controlled Release Volume 190,2014, 3-8

82. Neha Yadav , Sunil Khatak, Udai Vir Singh Sara, Solid Lipid Nanoparticles- A Review, International Journal of Applied Pharmaceutics. 2013, 8-18

83. Jeetendra Singh Negi,Pronobesh Chattopadhyay,Ashok Kumar Sharma,Veerma Ram. Development of solid lipid nanoparticles (SLNs) of lopinavir using hot self nano-emulsification (SNE) technique. European Journal of Pharmaceutical Sciences.48, 1–2, 2013, 231-239

84. Wolfgang Mehnert,Karsten Mader. Solid lipid nanoparticles: Production, characterization and applications. Advanced Drug Delivery Reviews.64,2012,83-101

85. Akanksha Garud, Deepti Singh, Navneet Garud. Solid Lipid Nanoparticles (SLN): Method, Characterization and Applications. International Current Pharmaceutical Journal 2012, 1(11): 384-393

86. Surajit Das, Wai Kiong NG, Parijat Kanaujia, Sanggu Kim, Reginald B.H. Tan. Formulation design, preparation and physicochemical characterizations of solid lipid nanoparticles containing a hydrophobic drug: Effects of process variables. Colloids and Surfaces B: Biointerfaces. 2011; 88:483– 489.

87. Diego Delgado, Ana del Pozo-Rodriguez, Maria Angeles Solinis, Alicia Rodriguez-Gascon. Understanding the mechanism of protamine in solid lipid nanoparticle-based lipofection: The importance of the entry pathway. European Journal of Pharmaceutics and Biopharmaceutics. 2011; 79: 495–502.

88. Sanju Dhawan, Rishi Kapil and Bhupinder Singh. Formulation development and systematic optimization of solid lipid nanoparticles of quercetin for improved brain delivery. Journal of Pharmacy and Pharmacology. 2011; 63: 342–351.

89. Ali Seyfoddin, John Shaw, and Raida Al-Kassas. Solid lipid nanoparticles for ocular drug delivery. Drug Delivery. 2010; 17(7): 467–489.

90. Ziyaur Rahman, Ahmed S. Zidan, Mansoor A. Khan. Non-destructive methods of characterization of risperidone solid lipid nanoparticles. European Journal of Pharmaceutics and Biopharmaceutics.2010; 76:127–137.

91. Hou Li Li, XiaoBin Zhao, YuKun Ma, Guang Xi Zhai, LingBing Li, HongXiang Lou. Enhancement of gastrointestinal absorption of quercetin by solid lipid nanoparticles. Journal of Controlled Release. 2009;133: 238–244

92. Qingzhi Lv, Aihua Yu, Yanwei Xi, Houli Li, Zhimei Songa, Jing Cui, Fengliang Cao, Guangxi Zhai. Development and evaluation of penciclovir-loaded solid lipid nanoparticles for topical delivery. International Journal of Pharmaceutics. 2009; 372: 191–198.

93. Jana Pardeike, Aiman Hommoss, Rainer H. Muller. Lipid nanoparticles (SLN, NLC) in cosmetic and pharmaceutical dermal products. International Journal of Pharmaceutics. 2009; 366: 170–184.

94. V. Jannin, J. Musakhanian, D. Marchaud. Approaches for the development of solid and semi-solid lipid-based formulations. Advanced Drug Delivery Reviews. 2008; 60:734–746.

95. Anthony A. Attama, Stephan Reichl, Christel C. Muller-Goymanna. Diclofenac sodium delivery to the eye: In vitro evaluation of novel solid lipid nanoparticle formulation using human cornea construct. International Journal of Pharmaceutics. 2008; 355: 307–313.

96. Indu Pal Kaur, Rohit Bhandari, Swati Bhandari, Vandita Kakkar. Potential of solid lipid nanoparticles in brain targeting. Journal of Controlled Release. 2008;127: 97–109

97. Jie Liu, Tao Gong, Hualin Fu, Changguang Wang, Xiuli Wang, Qian Chena, Qin Zhang, Qin He, Zhirong Zhang. Solid lipid nanoparticles for pulmonary delivery of insulin. International Journal of Pharmaceutics. 2008; 356: 333–344.

98. A. del Pozo-Rodriguez, D. Delgado, M.A. Solinis, A.R. Gascon, J.L. Pedraz. Solid lipid nanoparticles: Formulation factors affecting cell transfection capacity. International Journal of Pharmaceutics.2007; 339:261–268.

99. Antonio J. Almeida, Eliana Souto. Solid lipid nanoparticles as a drug delivery system for peptides and proteins. Advanced Drug Delivery Reviews. 2007; 59: 478–490.

100. Paolo Blasi, Stefano Giovagnoli, Aurelie Schoubben, Maurizio Ricci, Carlo Rossi. Solid lipid nanoparticles for targeted brain drug delivery. Advanced Drug Delivery Reviews. 2007; 59: 454–477.

101. Gisele A. Castro, Rodrigo L. Orefice, Jose M. C. Vilela, Margareth S. Andrade, & Lucas A. M. Ferreira. Development of a new solid lipid nanoparticle formulation containing retinoic acid for topical treatment of acne. Journal of Microencapsulation. 2007; 24(5): 395–407.

102. Jie Liu, Wen Hu, Huabing Chen, Qian Ni, Huibi Xu, Xiangliang Yang. Isotretinoin-loaded solid lipid nanoparticles with skin targeting for topical delivery. International Journal of Pharmaceutics. 2007; 328: 191–195.

103. Kumar A. Shah, Abhijit A. Date, Medha D. Joshi, Vandana B. Patravale. Solid lipid nanoparticles (SLN) of tretinoin: Potential in topical delivery. International Journal of Pharmaceutics. 2007; 345: 163–171.

104. Maria Antonietta Casadei ,Felice Cerreto,Stefania Cesa,Maria Giannuzzo,Michelle Feeney,Carlotta Marianecci, Patrizia Paolicelli. Solid lipid nanoparticles incorporated in dextran hydrogels: A new drug delivery system for oral formulations. International Journal of Pharmaceutics.2006,140-146

105. Catherine Charcosset, Assma El-Harati, Hatem Fessi. Preparation of solid lipid nanoparticles using a membrane contactor. Journal of Controlled Release. 2005; 108: 112– 120.

106. M.A. Schubert, C.C. Muller-Goymann. Characterisation of surface-modified solid lipid nanoparticles(SLN): Influence of lecithin and nonionic emulsifier. European Journal of Pharmaceutics and Biopharmaceutics.2005; 61: 77–86.

107. Rajesh Pandey, Sadhna Sharma, G.K. Khuller. Oral solid lipid nanoparticle-based antitubercular chemotherapy. Tuberculosis. 2005; 85: 415–420.

108. J.E. Kipp. The role of solid nanoparticle technology in the parenteral delivery of poorly water-soluble drugs. International Journal of Pharmaceutics. 2004; 284: 109–122.

109. Roberta Cavalli, M. Rosa Gasco, Patrizia Chetoni, Susi Burgalassi, M. Fabrizio Saettone. Solid lipid nanoparticles (SLN) as ocular delivery system for Tobramycin. International Journal of Pharmaceutics. 2002; 238: 241–245

110. Volkhard Jenning and Sven H. Gohla. Encapsulation of retinoids in solid lipid nanoparticles (SLN). J. microencapsulation. 2001; 18(2): 149–158.

111. Da-Bing CHEN, Tian-zhi YANG, Wang-Liang LU, and Qiang ZHANG. In Vitro and in Vivo Study of Two Types of Long-Circulating Solid Lipid Nanoparticles Containing Paclitaxel. Chem. Pharm. Bull. 2001; 49(11): 1444-1447.

112. Volkhard Jenning, Anja Gysler, Monika Schaefer-Korting, Sven H. Gohla. Vitamin A loaded solid lipid nanoparticles for topical use: occlusive properties and drug targeting to the upper skin. European Journal of Pharmaceutics and Biopharmaceutics. 2000; 49: 211-218.

113. C. Schwarz, W. Mehnert. Freeze-drying of drug-free and drug-loaded solid lipid nanoparticles (SLN). International Journal of Pharmaceutics. 1997; 157:171–179.

114. Roberta Cavalli, Otto Caputo, Maria Eugenia Carlotti, Michele Trotta, Carmela Scarnecchia, Maria Rosa Gasco. Sterilization and freeze-drying of drug-free and drug-loaded solid lipid nanoparticles. International Journal of Pharmaceutics. 1997; 148:47-54

115. Greenblatt DJ, Matlis R, Scavone JM, Blyden GT, Harmatz JS, Shader RI. "Oxaprozin pharmacokinetics in the elderly". British Journal of Clinical Pharmacology. 19 (3): 373–8.

116. http://www.nextbio.com/b/search/details/Oxaprozin?type=compound

117. https://www.drugbank.ca/drugs/DB00991

118. http://www.druglib.com/druginfo/daypro/description_pharmacology/

119. https://www.webmd.com/drugs/2/drug-6747/oxaprozin-oral/details

120. https://www.medicinenet.com/oxaprozin/article.htm#what_are_the_side_effects_of_oxaprozin

121. http://shodhganga.inflibnet.ac.in/jspui/bitstream/10603/188924/10/10_chapter %202.

122. https://www.chemicalbook.com/ChemicalProductProperty_EN_CB1242041.htm

123. https://www.lobachemie.com/fatty-acids-and-alcohols-06130/STEARIC-ACID-CASNO-57-11-4.aspx

124. Aminu Umar Kura, Samer Hasan Hussein-Al-Ali, Mohd Zobir Hussein, and Sharida Fakurazi. Preparation of Tween 80-Zn/Al-Levodopa-Layered Double Hydroxides Nanocomposite for Drug Delivery System. The Scientific World Journal Volume 2014, Article ID 104246, 10

125. Patil JS, Marapur SC, Kamalapur MV, Shiralshetti SS. Pharmaceutical product development and preformulation studies: early approaches, present scenario and future prospects. Research Journal of Pharmaceutical, Biological and Chemical Sciences. 2010;1(3): 782.

126. http://www.pharminfotech.co.nz/manual/Formulation/mixtures/pages/solubilities.html

127. Indian pharmacopeia. 2007; vol. 4.

128. http://www.chemspider.com/Chemical-Structure.4453.html.

129. Seda G. Sagdinca, Aslı Esmeb. Theoretical and vibrational studies of 4,5-diphenyl-2-2 oxazole propionic acid(oxaprozin). Spectrochimica Acta Part A75 (2010) 1370–1376.

130. M. Ganesh, B. Thangabalan, Dinesh Thakur, K. Srinivasan, Swstika Ganguly† and T. Sivakumar. UV Spectrophotometric Determination of Oxaprozin in Pure and Pharmaceutical Formulation. Asian Journal of Chemistry. 2008; 20(7):5451-5454.

131. Akanksha Garud, Deepti Singh, Navneet Garud, Solid Lipid Nanoparticles (SLN): Method, Characterization and Applications, International Current Pharmaceutical Journal 2012, 1(11): 384-393.

132. Melike Uner and Gulgun Yener, Importance of solid lipid nanoparticles (SLN) in various administration routes and future perspectives, Int J Nanomedicine. 2007; 2(3): 289–300.

133. Abdelbary G, Fahmy RH. Diazepam – loaded solid lipid nanoparticles: Design and characterization. AAPS PharmSciTech. 2009;10:211–9.

134. Heinzelmann ME, Wiesendanger R. Newyork: Springer verlogg; 1992. Scanning tunneling microscopy II surface science; 99–149.

135. Luo Y, Chen D, Ren L, Zhao X, Qin J. Solid lipid nanoparticles for enhancing vinpocetine's oral bioavailability. J Control Release. 2006; 114:53–9.

136. Hamed Hamishehkar, Mir Babak Bahadori, Somayeh Vandghanooni, Masoud Eskandani, Ailar Nakhlband, Morteza Eskandani. Preparation, characterization and anti-proliferative effects of sclareolloaded solid lipid nanoparticles on A549 human lung epithelial cancer cells. Journal of Drug Delivery Science and Technology. 45 (2018) 272–280.

Table of contents

Printed by Books on Demand GmbH, Norderstedt / Germany